Culture and Mental Disorders

Culture and

Mental Disorders

A Comparative Study of the Hutterites

and Other Populations

by Joseph W. Eaton, Ph.D.

IN COLLABORATION WITH

Robert J. Weil, M.D.

THE FREE PRESS, GLENCOE, ILLINOIS

Copyright 1955 by The Free Press, a corporation

Printed in the United States of America

DESIGNED BY SIDNEY SOLOMON

Library of Congress Catalog Card Number 55-7336

To Our Hutterite Friends

THEY MADE THIS STUDY POSSIBLE

Study Staff

Joseph W. Eaton	STUDY DIRECTOR AND SOCIOLOGIST
Robert J. Weil	PSYCHIATRIST
Bert Kaplan	PSYCHOLOGIST
Thomas F. A. Plaut	PSYCHOLOGIST
Evelyn McPuroff Plaut	FIELD WORK RESEARCH ASSISTANT AND PROJECT SECRETARY 1950-1951
William F. Pratt	FIELD WORK RESEARCH ASSISTANT 1950-1951
Helen Fay Eaton	FIELD WORK RESEARCH ASSISTANT SUMMERS 1950, 1951
Marvin Margolis	FIELD WORK RESEARCH ASSISTANT SUMMER 1951
Miriam Strassburger	FIELD WORK RESEARCH ASSISTANT SUMMER 1951
Jacob Driker	RESEARCH ASSISTANT 1949-1950
Bessie Weiss	PROJECT SECRETARY 1950-1951
Muriel Andrews	PROJECT SECRETARY 1951-1952
Mary Kemsley	PROJECT SECRETARY 1952-1953

Contents

[7]

Foreword

IN HIS famous book, *Civilization and Its Discontents*, Freud declined to offer his opinion as to whether civilization was the most precious thing we possess or too costly for the nature of man to endure. As he pointed out, we are foolishly developing and accumulating instruments and plans to destroy one another. Simultaneously mental illness becomes an ever-increasing problem in all civilized countries.

How much of our suicidal fears, individual and collective, and our illnesses can be ascribed to the group ideals and group attitudes and group living techniques that we have developed? Does our culture support us or does it bear so heavily upon some of us that they break under it, renouncing us all, our culture and our concept of reality? Or is it, perhaps, the intrinsic contradictions and conflicting values of the culture, and not its burdensomeness, which cause the individual to lose touch with reality? Or, finally, does it come back to something within the individual himself which is only indirectly related to his culture?

These are not rhetorical questions; they are research problems. I do not know the answers, any more than Freud did. I have heard many opinions; I have entertained some myself. But what I like about the study that Doctors Eaton and Weil have made is the fact that it offers some evidence, some data which provide a basis for a tentative opinion on this question. They are modest in their conclusions, these scientists, and they submit that culture does seem to have a major influence in shaping personality and the frequency of personality failures. This is a hypothesis to be tested by further researches.

Certainly these colleagues have studied carefully and competently an extraordinary phenomenon. Here are nearly nine thousand people scattered over North America, maintaining a common and rather unusual ideology which they translate into a way of life. They are highly civilized, reasonably intelligent, extraordinarily industrious and productive. They are Christians. They speak English. They read newspapers. They are in many ways like most of us.

But they do certain things very differently (from "us") and they believe it is important to do certain things and not to do certain things which the rest of the world does not believe to be so important. And they believe it all together.

Doctors Eaton and Weil have examined carefully what happens to the personal adjustment of people who grow up within this cultural mold. They spent several summers living with these people, talking with them, and observing them. They recorded their observations carefully, thoughtfully and comprehensively, and analyzed them. They found that the Hutterites are extraordinarily free of some forms of mental illness extremely common in the world at large. Why?

The implication is obviously that the price of our particular civilization as compared with that simpler or different civilization is more mental illness. Were I a Hutterite, I might word it this way: "Among the rewards of *our* way of living is a lower expectancy of mental illness." Knowing this fact, which set of values might a new arrival from Mars choose for himself?

Karl Menninger, M. D.

The Menninger Foundation
Topeka, Kansas

Acknowledgment

NO BOOK, and certainly not this study, could have been written without help from many persons and agencies. In this acknowledgment the writers wish to go beyond a public recognition of their great debt to those who gave significant aid to this undertaking. They also hope to provide the reader with a brief account of the institutional and intellectual milieu in which they worked, the setting in which the content of this book grew from a question-asking stage into a completed report—a basis for asking new questions at what we hope is a somewhat more advanced level of knowledge.

The book was written by the senior author. The psychiatric collaborator participated in much of the field work; he assumed final responsibility for the diagnosis of all cases of psychopathology and reviewed every draft of the study. Many of the ideas incorporated in this volume were first developed and explored in staff conferences in which the authors and every member of the study staff participated. Thomas F. A. Plaut played a particularly important part, devoting seemingly endless energy to this investigation in the field. Albert J. Mayer served as statistical consultant during the final period of analysis. Fortunately for this volume his fertile mind could not limit itself to the mere quantitative aspects of our data.

The book benefited greatly from detailed critical readings at various stages by Thomas F. Hoult, Edgar A. Schuler, and Donald Marsh, colleagues of the senior author at Wayne University. Virginia White, Jeremiah Kaplan, and Professor Joseph H. Friend of Western Reserve University, who share a healthy distaste for unnecessary technical language, read a final draft of this book and are responsible for many changes which improved both its content and its organization. James Clark Moloney, Paul Lemkau, Morton Kramer, John A. Clausen, Richard A. Schermerhorn and Arthur G. Steinberg made several valuable suggestions affecting the analysis of the data.

Our work was made possible through grants from the National Institute of Mental Health of the United States Public Health Service. The Department of Social Relations at Harvard University provided funds for one of the field workers in the summer of 1950. The study was sponsored by Wayne University. Dean Victor A. Rapport and Don S. Hecock, together with many other officials of Wayne's administrative staff, helped to solve many problems. Robert O. Jones, Chief, and other members of the Department of Psychiatry at Dalhousie University did much to facilitate the effective participation of the psychiatric collaborator in the conferences required for the analysis of our material.

Our study was nurtured by the opportunities for exchange of ideas at inter-disciplinary conferences of research workers on mental health problems held under the auspices of the Milbank Memorial Fund, the Social Science Research Council Committee on Social Psychiatry, the Grant Foundation, and the Work Conference in Mental Health Research. These conferences are a relatively new development in science. Research workers in the same field have at times jealously isolated their thoughts and findings until they could be pre-

sented to the public in published form. These meetings developed a preferred folkway of science, the process of mutual aid. We benefited from these discussions with other
investigators when aid was needed most—when the research
was in process and it was possible to act upon the advice and
criticisms of fellow scientists.

The Hutterite people gave freely of their time and hospitality to make this study possible without any promise or
expectation of reward. There were literally many hundreds
of individuals who gave significant aid, with a high level of
objectivity, honesty, and straightforwardness which, at times,
must have been very difficult for them. Our inquiry dealt
with personal affairs that are not ordinarily shared with outsiders and strangers. The Hutterites were willing to discuss
them in the conviction that their co-operation might make
possible a study which could have some broad humanitarian
implications. They accepted our staff with tolerance for our
right to be different without withholding their friendship.

To Edward A. Norman, who called the senior author's attention to the existence of the Hutterites and guided his
earlier investigation of their way of life, this study owes a
debt of affection and gratitude; the same applies to Nana
Goodhope. This scholarly and public-spirited grandmother,
wife of the village blacksmith of Viborg, first introduced the
writer in 1941 to the hospitable people of Jamesville Colony
in South Dakota.

No acknowledgment would be complete without mention
of the comradeship of our respective wives. Research demands
time and attention. It tends to intrude into normal home routine. If the study of the mental health of the Hutterites left
our family mental health intact, much of the credit goes to
their help and support.

JWE
RJW

1.

The Cultural Approach in Psychiatry

MENTAL disorders have been less affected by the steady pace of medical progress than most other threats to human health. The prevention or cure of other illnesses, particularly those of a communicable and infectious nature, is reaching the point where some, like smallpox, syphilis, and tetanus, are being eliminated as major health hazards. More people can now live to an age when the risk of mental illness becomes great. Goldhamer and Marshall[1] have shown that approximately one in fifteen persons in New York State in 1940 who lived to be 65 years of age has spent some time in a mental hospital. Landis and Page stated that "One of every ten Americans is likely to suffer a serious mental difficulty which will incapacitate them during some part of their lives."[2] The Hospital Committee of the Group for Advancement of Psychiatry estimated that there were eight and a half million psychiatric cases in the United States during the early 1940's.[3] In 1950 about 55 per cent of the patient days in all hospitals were spent by mental patients.[4] In modern America, mental disorders rank high among the severely disabling illnesses in terms of cost, number of persons involved, chronicity, and suffering. Can this fact be a consequence of the pace of modern living? Were mental disorders less prevalent among past generations who lived in a simpler rural world? Are there some "ideal" cultures where psychic disturbances are relatively rare? These popular questions imply a common theory about cause—the theory that culture and social relationships are deeply involved in the multidimensional causal pattern.

Not many would quarrel with the general proposition that the social setting in which men live and the things they believe are correlated with many of the symptoms of mental pathology. Even a superficial review of hospital, police, and census reports shows that human groups differ widely in their *observed* rates of mental and personality disorders. There is far less agreement about what these variations mean. The questions of *why* and *how* mental disorders are related to cultural pressures, therefore, require intensive investigation. Even a partial answer might lead to insights that could result in improvements of presently inadequate methods of prevention, treatment, and cure.

Much of our present-day knowledge of mental disorders has come from observing patients after they became mentally ill outside the setting in which they fell ill. This book is based on a study of an entire social system in which the healthy as well as the sick in the population were studied. Much was known about the entire group, its culture, its values, its demography, and its history to provide insights into the connection that may exist between culture and mental disorders. The work was done under conditions of control of certain dependent variables to a degree unusual in social research with human beings. Our laboratory was the Hutterite sect of North America. Our immediate objective was to find all cases of mental disorder known to have occurred among living members. Our method was to compare these findings with somewhat comparable information from other groups. We also looked for common clinical trends in Hutterite case histories which could be related to major culture patterns.

This approach to the study of diseases, the method of comparing their frequency, their patterns, and their distribution in different populations, is technically referred to as *epidemiological*. It assumes that each group can be viewed as a natural laboratory in which factors of illness and health maintain a balance. If the balance in one group seems to differ significantly from that in another, this difference is a clue that can lead scientists to the detection of factors promoting or inhibiting the disorder. Goldberger's dramatic use of epidemiological clues to explain, control, and prevent pellagra is perhaps the best known psychiatric example.[5] There can be no guarantee that the same approach will also be effective with other mental disorders, but there is reason for optimism. Mental disorders are definitely not distributed at random throughout the human race. If more can be learned about the precise nature of these population differences, plausible and experimentally testable hypotheses are likely to emerge which can put scientists on the trail of new knowledge in a field now enveloped in mystery and obscurity.[6]

Culture and social relationships are suspected of playing a role in "triggering off" the onset of organic mental illnesses like many of those associated with old age, but the assumption that sociological factors are causal is most widely held for functional mental disorders. It has been stated in terms analogous to those of individualistic psychiatry by persons who regard some cultures as being either healthy or sick mentally. The mental hygiene expert Lawrence K. Frank,[7] in his book *Society as the Patient*, refers to the American culture as being ". . . sick, mentally disordered and in need of treatment." Read Bain,[8] a sociologist, speaks of "Our Schizoid Culture." He regards the irrational and contradictory norms of Americans as "neurotic and psychotic societal behavior." The first empirical analysis of suicide statistics by Emile Durkheim shows that there is support for a theory that social cohesion can provide psychic support to individuals who undergo severe personal trauma, and that suicide rates are a function of anomie—the absence of such social support.[9] Robert K. Merton has proposed a more general theoretical formulation to explain how the social structure of a group exerts pressure upon individuals to become conformists or innovators if they accept the normative cultural goals, or to show their rejection of these goals through ritualistic, retreatist, or rebellious behavior.[10] These theoretical approaches, which all claim that culture and social relationships are dynamic (or causal) factors in producing socially deviant or mentally disordered individuals, are supported by evidence from a number of scientific disciplines.

Mental disorders are abnormal psychological manifestations of the personality. Personality develops in the child and the adult through interaction with their culture. Studies in the area of culture and personality indicate that normal, as well as criminal, delinquent, and other forms of antisocial behavior, are related to cultural factors.[11] Such forms of antisocial behavior have much in common with mental disorders. They are usually without organic cause; they are learned responses, and they tend to be very disturbing to both the patient and his environment. If culture is a causal factor in antisocial behavior, the hypothesis of a similar relationship for functional mental disorders is plausible.

Sociologists and biometricians have noted that observed frequencies of mental disorders are significantly correlated with certain social variables, such as age, sex, social class, economic status, occupation, ecological area of residence, marital status, ethnic group membership, and other factors. A correlation of social categories and those of a mental disease is no proof of causal interrelation, but it suggests the possibility. The social-psychiatric view of Jurgen Ruesch and Gregory Bateson that ". . . psychopathology is defined in terms of disturbances of communication"[12] provides a plausible theory for explaining correlations of the frequency of mental disorders with sociological factors. Social groups probably differ widely in the readiness and training of members to perceive, evaluate and transmit ideas. They also vary in the learning and socialization processes which are facilitated and which shape the channels of communication in individuals and between them. Groups with a high degree of homogeneity and strong common values facilitate interpersonal communication far more and in a qualitatively different manner than those which lack these qualities.

Mental disorders have been and are being studied carefully by medical men. Often they are searching for genetic, organic, glandular, psychosomatic, or neurological factors that might have causal significance. Some are known to exist. But they are never adequate as a total explanation. No one develops general paresis without having had syphilis, but not all persons with such an organic infection develop general paresis. There is evidence of familial tendencies in the transmission of some psychoses, mental defects, and epilepsy. Familial transmission, however, is not necessarily conclusive proof of genetic causality. By a process of elimination, the question arises: "What other factors might be etiologically significant?" The socio-cultural environment is one possible answer.

Anthropologists and psychiatrists have reported the virtual absence of certain mental disorders in some primitive social systems. Moloney[13] believed the Okinawans to be relatively immune to psychoses and quoted others who have described the Dyaks of Borneo, the Lepchas in the Himalayan Mountains, and the natives of Truk Island as being relatively mature emotionally. Weinberg[14] points out that Robert Faris, Cooper, Devereaux, and Seligman claim schizophrenia to be rare or nonexistent in homogeneous nonliterate societies having minimal contact with Western cultures. Elsworth Faris thinks this to be true for the Bantu people of the African Congo forest because of their intimate social relationships.

The relative rarity of observed cases of schizophrenia in such cultures is attributed by Devereaux to their consistent value structure and their "one answer" universe. Kardiner reports a virtual nonexistence of depression and suicide among the Alorese. Similar observations were made by Carothers in Kenya, in East Africa. Cases of schizophrenia but no manic depressions among the Tembu people were reported by Laubscher. Carothers and Seligman speculated further that schizophrenia tends to become manifest in those primitive populations who are exposed to close culture contacts with Europeans and are, as a result, experiencing drastic social changes. This study of the Hutterites in North America was begun on the basis of their reputation of being virtually free of psychotic breakdowns and antisocial activities, although, unlike the previously-mentioned groups, the Hutterites are not technologically primitive.

These social-anthropological observations are of uncertain validity. Most of them are based on studies in which there was somewhat limited culture contact, without sampling controls. The frequency of mental disorders cannot be determined without a population census. This is a technically difficult research problem even in an American setting, where there are some diagnostic facilities and hospital records, and where fewer barriers of language and values confront the anthropologist than in similar work among primitive groups. The evidence from social psychology, sociology, medicine, and anthropology makes plausible the theory that culture and social relationships are major dynamic factors. The relationships, however, need not be direct.

There are several partly non-sociological methods of explanation which also need be explored. They are not mutually exclusive, and probably all are pertinent to some degree. For example, the tendency for manifesting some mental disorders may be transmitted genetically.[15] Glass[16] has demonstrated that in man genetic qualities can be reinforced by cultural factors which affect mate selection. They may be intensified through inbreeding or become rare through outbreeding. This process, which is technically referred to as *genetic drift*, is a consequence of stable and long-term cultural trends in the choice of marriage partners. It results in a gradual increase or decrease in the frequency distribution of genetic potentialities present in the original group.

Other cultural factors, such as public welfare services, the addition of iodine to table salt, or the absence of safety inspection laws in factories, also may have indirect consequences for mental disorders. Such forces help to protect from or expose to injury, infection, or metabolic diseases which can lead to "purely" organic, glandular, or neurological abnormalities with psychological manifestations.

Sociological factors can also intensify or minimize conflicts related to psychological drives, which are thought by many to have a bearing on some mental disorders. Two common examples are sex and aggression. These basic drives, with which many mental patients cannot cope appropriately in terms of the expectations of their group, are culturally conditioned. Cultures can and do vary greatly in the degree to which they provide channels for expression of those psychological impulses in socially approved ways.

Variations in frequency of mental disorders in different population samples can also be due to sampling error. Differences as large as or larger than 100 per cent are not necessarily significant if they are based on a rare phenomenon and a relatively small population base. For example, in 1951 we found 53 cases of psychosis among 8,542 persons, or 0.62 per cent, of the Hutterite population. If it could be assumed that this phenomenon is distributed at random throughout any population, the confidence limits at the 1 per cent level would be from 34 to 72 cases. This means that in 99 out of 100 such samples the true parameter or count would range from 34 to 72 cases. At the 5 per cent level the confidence limits would be from 39 to 67. Differences within these limits might be significant, but on a statistical basis alone they would not be. We know that mental diseases are not randomly distributed. Variations due to sampling error alone could well exceed the frequency differences observed in any of the studies made so far. This fact should not discourage research in a field where large samples cannot be observed. It does not preclude the possibility that differences found are significant. Many scientific results began with statistically nonsignificant findings which proved to be truly significant.

Finally, many of the variations in the frequency of mental disorders are without doubt a spurious consequence of variations in diagnostic standards, treatment facilities, completeness of patient enumeration, and willingness of the people to co-operate in the surveys. For example, Page and Landis[17] report that, although there is no clear evidence that the true prevalence of mental disorders has increased, the resident population of civil mental hospital in New York State has grown steadily from 1910 through 1940. This fact was made possible by an *increase in the bed capacity* of mental hospitals.

The analyst of epidemiological data on mental disorders is confronted with a multiple correlation problem which in reality is far more complex than the interplay of factors that have been sketched briefly in this chapter. It is impossible to isolate any of these factors in an even remotely "pure" state, unaffected by the operations of other factors. Human beings, culture, and social life cannot be broken down into basic elements like a complex organic molecule. The only "laboratory" available for the study of such entities as *culture* and *mental disorders* is a human social system which has many attributes other than the two of primary concern to this investigation. The factors that have been referred to are only some of the variables that could contribute to an understanding of our data. They are logical constructs or analytical models, useful because they can be a basis for making inferences about relationships; they make possible the testing of hypotheses. The tests, however, can be made only under conditions of moderate control of some of the dependent variables.

Despite the difficulties which confront investigators in this, as in all other social science problems, there is reason for optimism. It may be possible to locate psychiatrically significant control points of culture through patient detective work. The discovery of direct or even circumstantial evidence that some mental disorders are significantly related to specific culture patterns may be important not only in itself, as is any advancement in human knowledge; it can lead to new ways of inquiry into the psychiatric problems that remain unanswered.

The selection of sociological variables for special attention does not imply any denial of those fairly well established findings in psychiatry which show that mental disorders often involve psychodynamic, organic, and genetic processes. The writers of this book accept the multidisciplinary point of view that all human behavior is a complex process which can be viewed simultaneously from several levels of abstraction. Our focus is primarily on the cultural and social dimensions, but far less insight would have been gained into the problems of mental disorders if there had been no recognition of the importance of other human behavior variables. The writers could not analyze their data with the view of certain intellectually insulated psychiatric cults that mental disorders, perhaps the most complex of human behaviors, can be explained adequately by reference to a few factors or even to one. They could not accept the assumption in some psychiatric circles that culture and most social relationships can be dismissed as almost irrelevant to the diagnosis and treatment of mental disorders.

2.

The Hutterites as a Laboratory

An Autonomous Culture

MANY of their neighbors take the Hutterites as much for granted as the landscape, scarcely worthy of notice except perhaps for an occasional remark concerning their idiosyncrasies. They are an ethnic group with several centuries of continuity in biological descent and with distinctive social and cultural traditions.[18] To the social scientist their quaint cooperative and theocratic social system blossoming in the American West offered a unique opportunity to study complex culture-personality problems in a fairly controlled and responsive social setting. The writers enjoyed, with some very few exceptions, the intelligent co-operation of the entire population of the sect. In accordance with their religious emphasis on helping others, they gave freely of their time and hospitality, with no expectation or promise of reward. They were not only objects of study but also collaborators who helped actively in working out certain problems.

The validity of any cross-cultural generalizing is limited by many uncontrollable variables. There are great differences between what the Hutterites call "the world" and "our Gemein"

(Community). The Hutterite sect, unlike American Indian tribes or other folk societies which have been studied by anthropologists in cross-cultural surveys, has a way of life which is much more similar to the larger American scene. We cannot present a complete picture of Hutterite customs within the limits of this book. The reader with a special interest in sociology and anthropology will find many social and cultural data in Chapters 11 and 12 of this book, which deal with *Hutterite "Psychiatry"* and *The Impact of Social Change on Mental Health*. But a summary of the more distinctive culture patterns is presented here as a necessary background for the interpretation of our findings.

Before we emphasize certain unusual features of the Hutterite social system, it must be noted that it is not "primitive" in the ethnographic sense. Hutterites employ some of the most up-to-date machinery. They are informed about the work of agricultural experiment stations and sometimes seek their advice. The people are literate in both their native Germanic dialect and in English. Their children attend school to the eighth grade. The schools are parochial but are staffed by licensed, generally non-Hutterite, elementary teachers. Nearly all the members are native citizens of the United States or Canada. They and their forebears have been exposed to American ways of living for over seventy-five years. They share with the majority of Americans the general Judaeo-Christian heritage of Western civilization. Hutterite values and beliefs have much in common with those of other contemporary orthodox religious groups such as rural French Catholics, ultra-orthodox Jews, Seventh Day Adventists, and Mennonites.

Hutterites believe in the communal ownership and control of all property. Like the Catholic orders, they live under economic communism in the classical and nonpolitical sense. Christ and the Bible are their ideological guides. Hutterites expect the community to assume a great deal of responsibility for each member. It is the community which buys clothing, doles out pocket money to each person, and pays a traffic ticket. No wages are paid. Each person is expected to work to the best of his ability. He eats his meals in the community dining room; the meals prepared by different women in rotation. If he is sick, the colony pays for all necessary care. In case of male death, widows and dependents have no financial worries; the loss of a breadwinner never means the loss of bread. The Hutterite way of life provides social security from the womb to the tomb. The religious creed of the group gives the members a further guarantee of security beyond the tomb. It promises absolute salvation to all who follow its precepts.

The average Hutterite baby is delivered at home with a midwife in attendance and by "natural childbirth." Ultimately he will have between ten and eleven siblings. Children are generally wanted. Birth control practices are considered sinful; violations of this taboo are extremely rare. There is much communal co-operation in the care and education of the children. Infants are looked after by the mother for the first two months after birth. Then the mother must work part of each day in the community kitchen or garden, and an older girl, not necessarily a relative, helps out. After the age of two and a half, all healthy youngsters attend a communal kindergarten, where they stay most of the day. When they reach school age, they continue to spend many of their waking hours as a group, often under the supervision of a Hutterite religious teacher. He is responsible for much of the discipline outside of the hours when the children attend public school. Since both mother and father work for the colony at least part of each day, older siblings assume much of the care of their younger brothers and sisters.

In general, young people do a great deal of their growing up within a stable and closely-knit group of peers. The process of socialization and development depends greatly on "horizontal" identification with their peer group. Imagination and expectations are influenced considerably by other children of similar physical and mental development. The Hutterite nuclear family performs fewer functions than is general in American society, but there is strong emphasis on kinship ties in all social relations. The cultural pattern of growing up to become a Hutterite adult varies little from colony to colony, but as in every human group, there are important variations in the emotional relationships between parents and children. Two mothers may be equally determined to teach an eight-year-old daughter to be an efficient caretaker of the baby and resist the temptation to run off in the yard to play with boys of her age (who have no such similar work expectations to live up to); but where one mother may teach and discipline with patience, humor, and love, another may be vindictive and infantile, almost forgetful of the fact that an eight-year-old girl is still a child.

Virtually all Hutterites leave school on their fifteenth birthday, the day which marks their assignment to an adult job. Full membership status is acquired after baptism, between the ages of 18 and 25. Very few people remain single. Several decades ago parents and community leaders exerted some influence on the choice of marriage partners; at present, however, this is rare. After marriage men tend to acquire more prestige and are given more responsible work assignments. They are put in charge of the carpentry, welding shop, horses, pigs, or some other department of the large-scale community farm enterprise. Women begin to raise a family. They also acquire more prestige in the informal discussions which precede all formal community decisions. Women can retire from regular community chores at the age of 45; retirement for men takes place later. No one is pushed to exert himself much beyond what he himself regards to be his capacity. "Do the best you can," rather than a competitive slogan, is characteristic of the entire life cycle.

All Hutterites live in small and nearly self-sufficient settlements in which social relationships are generally informal or primary. They have an average of 92 members, with 16 family units. There is virtually no movement from one to another, except for women at marriage when, with few exceptions, they move to the husband's community. Most members of the sect spend their entire life within the same group. When a community grows too large through natural increase, new land is purchased and another village is built. Half the membership, chosen by lot, "swarm" to form a new "hive," as Hutterites like to refer to this process of binary fission.* In each of the 93 settlements there are individual differences in prestige, which are largely a function of age, sex, and work. However, this society comes as close to being classless as any we know.

The colony government can be characterized as a *patriarchal democracy*. Each adult member has some initiative and authority in his field or work, but only men have a formal vote. Controversial issues are usually discussed informally for a long time by both men and women. Decisions are not often made if there is strong opposition, even from a substantial female minority. Government is more by consensus than by power. The business manager, called *Wirt* in the Germanic dialect, is referred to as *boss* in English. He is elected to his position by a majority vote of all adult baptized males and is given a great deal of executive discretion in the day-to-day management of colony affairs. Most *bosses* hold their posts for several decades until old age makes their retirement necessary. Before making a decision, generally they are careful to consult informally with any member affected.

In spiritual affairs, the elected preacher assumes primary leadership. He and the *boss* are the top management team and

---

* Five new colonies were established between September 1, 1951, and February 1, 1953, bringing the total number of settlements to 98.

serve to keep tab on each other's activities. In many communities checks require the signature of both to be negotiable. (In a few cases the position of *boss* and preacher are held by the same person.) The preacher is nominated by a vote in which not only the male members of a village but also leaders of other villages participate. The final choice among the nominees is made by lot from those receiving a substantial (previously specified) proportion of the vote. The post is held for life. Hutterites believe that preachers are chosen by God, but nomination of candidates by ballot indicates that they wish to give the Lord a helping hand.

There is much emphasis on religion. Church services are held every day and are attended by almost every older child and adult. Prayers are offered before and after every meal. Religious beliefs, which are similar to those of the Amish, Mennonites, and other Anabaptist groups, stress pacifism, adult baptism, and simplicity in consumption and recreation. The culture is orthodox, integrated around an absolute value system. No major deviation from central beliefs and socially approved practices is tolerated. Each generation is indoctrinated systematically to grow up to believe and live as close to tradition as possible. The basic orientation is not to change but to maintain the status quo. The needs of the group tend to take precedence in most situations over the wants of any individual. Children, whose education during the day is under community auspices, are subjected to a continuous, uniform, but generally rote form of religious indoctrination. Faith is often more a consequence of institutionalized habit than of dynamic conviction. People are not usually converted to the Hutterite faith; they are born into it.

Hutterites never escape the sense of feeling "different" or being so regarded by their neighbors. Their hamlets, which they call "colonies," are geographically separate from non-Hutterite settlements in the area. This segregation is reinforced by many distinctive practices, like their hair styles and home-made clothing. Men wear black home-made pants; women never go out without their polka-dotted kerchiefs. Members rarely go to town for any reason other than to do business, see a doctor, or pick up the colony mail. Non-Hutterites generally regard the brethren as inferior because they are different; Hutterites regard many of their neighbors as spiritually contaminated or misguided by decadent "modern ways." Their relationships are focussed almost exclusively on business; social intercourse is usually not encouraged by either group.

We do not wish to overstate the degree of homogeneity of behavior, values, and expectations within the group. Hutterites are not made in one mold. Those who penetrate the barriers of communication inherent in cultural differences find numerous individual variations. Our field observations and projective tests show evidence of considerable spontaneity and imagination in interpersonal relations. Only by comparison with the more diversified American or Western European cultures can that of the Hutterites be characterized as being relatively uniform.

Genetic and Social Selection

Hereditary predispositions are suspected of playing a role in the etiology of some mental disorders. It is, therefore, important to note that there has probably been some gene concentration among contemporary Hutterites. Since the end of the eighteenth century, religion and history have worked together to make the sect an almost self-contained bio-social mating unit. Incest is absolutely taboo; but the influx of outsiders, or what Hutterites call "new blood," has been minute, particularly since the group settled in the United States three quarters of a century ago. Families with variant traditions, aspirations, and living patterns have not been freely absorbed. In 1950 there were only fifteen patronyms in the entire sect.*

---

* On the basis of reports from about 95 per cent of the population, the

Three names—Hofer, Waldner, and Wipf—accounted for nearly half the families.

Since 1930, thirty individuals of non-Hutterite ethnic stock (eleven adult converts and nineteen children) have joined the group. Some of the children of these converts have recently married ethnic Hutterites. There have been 34 births in such "mixed" marriages. This group of sixty-four (converts plus children of marriages involving a convert) was less than one per cent of the ethnic population in 1950. In view of their variant cultural and ethnic background they have been excluded from the study.†

Some Hutterites stated that they believe there is "bad" blood in the group. They blame in-group mating for most of their cases of mental defect and certain psychoses. After World War II one of their preachers traveled several thousand miles to investigate the possibility of adopting European war orphans who would bring "fresh" blood into the sect. In some colonies converts are welcomed for the same biological reason, but the close-knit familial traditions of the group make it difficult for an adult outsider to be readily assimilated. Full acceptance is a slow process.

That the tendency to inbreed began several centuries ago

---

relative frequency of Hutterite family surnames is as follows:

Hofer	22.4%	Kleinsasser	5.8%	Entz	4.2%
Waldner	17.2%	Tschetter	5.8%	Wollman	3.9%
Wipf	9.7%	Gross	5.7%	Decker	1.2%
Stahl	6.6%	Walter	5.1%	Glanzer	1.0%
Wurz	6.2%	Mandel	4.5%	Knels	0.7%

† Hutterites do not engage in missionary activities. However, in Paraguay, Bolivia, England, and Ontario, Canada, there are autonomous groups of pacifists who have adopted the name "Hutterite" because their communal way of life and religious convictions approximate those of the ethnic Hutterites. They come from many ethnic backgrounds; they are generally well-educated men and women who grew up in the "world" but were searching for a solution to personal religious problems. These converts have little contact with the American Hutterites except for occasional visits and correspondence with some of their leaders. For more details see: Joseph Winfield Fretz, *Pilgrims in Paraguay* (Scottdale, Pennsylvania: Herald Press, 1953), pp. 53-60.

is supported by circumstantial historical evidence.[19] The Hutterite sect had its origin in 1528 in Switzerland during the Protestant reformation. In the middle of the 16th century Hutterite church records report that the sect grew through conversion until there were about eighty colonies, mostly in Moravia, numbering about 13,000-15,000 "souls." The believers always differentiated themselves from the people among whom they lived. From the very beginning they endured persecution, including, in many cases, death at the stake. Among those so killed was Jacob Huter, the leader whose name the sect adopted after his martyrdom in 1536.

During the 17th century most Hutterites had to flee from Moravia. Many went to Hungary, only to meet persecution again as the influence of Austrian Jesuits increased there. By 1762 a calculated policy of hostility had almost annihilated the sect; the number of active Hutterites was reduced to thirteen adults. They fled with nothing but their lives to Wallachia, in modern Rumania, then a Turkish province. At the time Turkey was a haven of tolerance for many Christian religious deviants. In 1762 this small remnant of Hutterites was joined by 49 Carinthian Lutherans who had also been forced to flee from Jesuit wrath. Ideologically the Hutterites absorbed the larger group, but the latter gradually assumed active leadership.

During the Turkish-Russian war of 1769-1774 these people had to migrate again. They were offered refuge in the Ukraine, in Russia, under the regime of Catherine the Great. The Czarina was eager to motivate skilled artisans and farmers to settle in her realm. The Hutterites received economic aid and guarantees of religious freedom. In Russia they lived in separate villages for about a century, making no effort to assimilate. There is no record of Hutterite conversion of Russians or their absorption into the group. The Hutterites regarded themselves as culturally and spiritually superior to their indigenous, and mostly illiterate, peasant neighbors.

There seemed to have been no necessity for close contact with Russians. Symptomatic of this may be the fact that the American linguist and historian A. J. F. Zieglschmid found only about a hundred words of Russian derivation in their current or past speech and writings.[19] The Hutterites had contact, through occasional visiting and correspondence, with a group of Anabaptist Germans who lived in East Prussia. A widow and her daughter, as well as an orphan boy named Entz, were taken into the group during the early decades of the 19th century. The contemporary families named Entz, 4.2 per cent of the total population, are reputed to be descendants of this orphan convert. It is possible that some other new members came into the group; many ethnically German Mennonite farmers lived in the same vicinity. Hutterite chronicles, however, contain no record of such an influx. They make reference only to co-operation between the two sects in their dealings with Russian governmental authorities.

Although modern Hutterites appear to be the biological descendants of a small group of Protestant dissidents who settled in Russia nearly two centuries ago, the net effect of this fact on genetic predispositions must not be exaggerated. The variability of gene permutations in man is very great, and concentration of genetic potentials is a very slow process.

Development of Contemporary Subgroups

The in-group marriage patterns were not disturbed when the entire group left Russia for the United States between 1874 and 1877. Contemporary descendants of the early Hutterite settlers are divided into two clearly distinct groups, the colony Hutterites and the *Prairieleut*, or *Hutterite Mennonites*. Originally these groups were differentiated largely on the basis of their attitude towards communal living. Today they have little in common and have few contacts with each other. The split dates back to the second decade of the nineteenth century. All Hutterites were then living in one community in Roditschawa, twenty miles from Wischenka, in South Russia. They were in economic difficulty, and there was considerable conflict and factionalism within the group. When all their community buildings were destroyed by a fire in 1819, the people no longer had enough enthusiasm to rebuild these common facilities. They decided to disband, and the land was divided into family homesteads. The communal economy came to an end, but ties of common religion, history, and kinship remained.

In 1843 the Hutterites moved to new and better land in southern Russia, near Melitopol. They founded three villages, Hutterthal, Johannesruh, and Neu-Hutterthal. Each family had its own farm, but among many of the householders there were pangs of conscience. The persons and issues which had led to the abandonment of community living were dead. The belief was still strongly held that eternal salvation could be obtained only by those who followed the example of Christ and his apostles as told in Acts 2:44-45: "And all that believed were together and had all things in common. And sold their possessions and goods and parted them to all men, as every man had need." Several of the younger men led a revival movement. During the years 1859-60 two groups of families, each under the leadership of a preacher, pooled their belongings. But not all the families took their faith quite so seriously; many did not join the revived communal property arrangement.

In 1870 Czar Alexander II announced the abrogation of the exemptions from military service and from use of the Russian language in schools which had been granted to the Hutterites under Catherine the Great. The group looked for a new haven of refuge; they found it in the United States. Between 1874 and 1877 all Hutterites left Russia. Those families whose belief in the principle of communal living was strong joined in building one of three communal villages. Others settled in the prairie nearby on individual homesteads.

In 1880 the United States census enumerated 443 Hutterites living in four colonies. The number of *Prairieleut* exceeded them, but there are no similarly precise data.

There was some movement into and out of the colonies during the first two decades after their establishment. Ten family groups are known to have joined them between 1880 and 1895, including the male ancestors of all families named Tschetter, who constituted nearly 6 per cent of the 1950 population. Seven, very much smaller family groups, left before 1918. The net effect of the known in-and-out migration prior to 1918 can be shown most clearly if the membership of the colonies of 1880 is correct for individuals who were then alive and who joined or left the sect before 1918. Instead of the 443 persons enumerated by the 1880 census, there would have been 472, an increase of 6.5 per cent.

The cultural gap between the colony group and the *Prairieleut* widened as the years went by. Their movement into colonies stopped before the turn of the century. After two decades of living on an individualistic basis in America, the problem of adjustment to colony life became so difficult that, as far as we know, none of the Hutterite Mennonites have joined a colony since that time.

The Hutterite religion forbids marriages with nonmembers of the church. Hutterites also have a strict moral code. It is not likely that illicit sexual relations have been a factor in modifying the genetic composition of the group. Adolescents are carefully watched. Control through conscience and parental prohibitions is particularly effective among young girls. We do not know of any case where a woman now living in a Hutterite colony is reputed to have been made pregnant by an "outsider."

This study deals, therefore, exclusively with the descendants of the original colony Hutterites and those of their kin who joined them before 1895. However, the *Prairieleut* could serve as a control group for certain purposes. Although their contemporary descendants are closely related ethnically and genetically to the colony people, they have led a very different cultural and economic life since their arrival in the United States. They are rapidly assimilating, but many still live in southeastern South Dakota. The *Prairieleut* can be readily identified by their membership in Hutterite Mennonite congregations.

The probability of endogamy (in-group marriage) is further enhanced by the division of colony Hutterites into three clannish kinship groups. Marriages now rarely take place between them, even though all of them consider themselves to be of the same faith and ethnic background. They are named *Schmiedenleut*, *Lehrerleut*, and *Dariusleut* respectively, after the name or occupation of their first leaders. They originated as social cliques in Russia and when they migrated to America, each clique formed a separate colony. As they grew in number through natural increase, each "mother" colony split to form "daughter" colonies. Every settlement is an autonomous economic unit, but within each kinship group there is considerable inter-colony mutual aid. Each group has its own bishop and a council of ministers which can make rules binding on all members. In 1950 the *Schmiedenleut* were settled in South Dakota, North Dakota, and Manitoba; the *Lehrerleut* and the *Dariusleut* colonies were in Montana and Alberta. Their geographical distribution is shown in Figure 1.

Before World War I, when all Hutterites lived in southeastern South Dakota, there were occasional marriages between members of different kinship groups. Even then they were rare, despite the small number of available prospective marriage partners within each clique. By 1950 each kinship group had developed seemingly slight, but to the Hutterites well-known, differences in dress, colony organization, degree of readiness to accept modern technology, and intimacy of contact with non-Hutterite neighbors. Most of the business and social ties are between colonies *within* the same kinship group. Few business and even fewer social ties exist *between* members of different kinship groups.

In-group mating would tend to accentuate the frequency of those mental disorders which might involve one or more recessive genetic factors. The Hutterite culture counteracts this tendency to some extent by discouraging procreation of persons who clearly show signs of mental disturbance

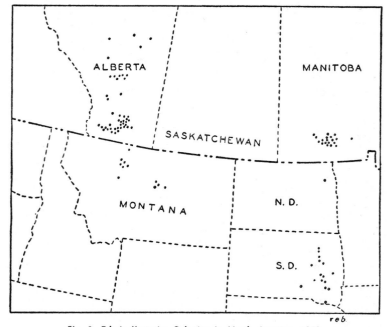

Fig. 1. Ethnic Hutterite Colonies in North America: 1950

when they are young. Of the 129 adults thirty years old or over who were enumerated as being or having been psychotic, neurotic, mentally defective, epileptic, or affected by a personality disorder, 14 per cent were single, as against about 5 per cent in the same age group of all Hutterites living in the summer of 1951. The state of "single blessedness" was particularly high among the adult borderline mental defectives (55 per cent) and schizophrenics (29 per cent).

Marital ties are never broken, even if the illness strikes after marriage, as it usually does in manic-depressive or neurotic depressive reactions. Married patients well enough to maintain sexual relations procreate without restrictions. Hutterite religious beliefs would not approve of eugenic rationalization for birth control. Social factors such as poverty, high accident rates, and high mortality, which reduce the net natural increase of handicapped persons in the American society, take much less of a toll in the families of similarly handicapped Hutterites. The communal way of life offers them considerable protection.

Throughout the centuries of Hutterite history cultural and genetic drift factors have reinforced each other. The distinctive and separatist tendencies of the Hutterite way of life have favored in-group breeding; at the same time the high prevalence of kinship ties within the group has simplified the process of maintaining a common core of culture.

Population Stability

Human mobility introduces into studies of mental disorder morbidity a bias whose effect cannot normally be estimated adequately. For example, Robert E. L. Faris and H. Warren Dunham[20] in their pioneer study of ecological factors in mental disease, found that the incidence of schizophrenia was highest in Chicago slum areas. They posed the question: Is schizophrenia a disorder more likely to strike people who live in slums, or are schizoid personalities likely to drift into slums, so that upon hospitalization they are recorded as slum residents? The writers were unable to control their population sample for migration to answer this question to their own satisfaction.

In contrast, the Hutterite social system has been characterized by a high degree of stability in membership. The unusual details of Hutterite demographic composition and history, recently published by Joseph W. Eaton and Albert J. Mayer,[21] need not be repeated here. In general, the available data indicates that a study of mental health could be made in this population with considerable control over the effects of migration factors on morbidity or disease rates.* The net effect of migration prior to 1918, as has been indicated previously, was to add about 6.5 per cent to the colony population of 1880. Our data on out-migration since 1918 is less complete than that on in-migration, but it provides a basis for estimating the effect on mental disorder morbidity rates. In 1951 all living persons were enumerated who were born in a colony since 1874-77 but left the sect. We have information on 106 Hutterite males and eight females who "deserted," as the Hutterites put it. This is nearly one of every 20 males over fourteen years of age, and one of every 250 females. Together they represent about 2.5 per cent of all ethnic Hutterites aged 15 and over.† Whenever possible we inquired about the social and psychological adjustment of these

---

* Two complete population enumerations were made, encompassing between them almost the entire history of the sect in North America. A microfilm copy of the 1880 census for the South Dakota counties in which Hutterites had settled was obtained. It was possible to identify all 443 persons then living in colonies and thus make an exact count of the population by age and sex. The records also included information about their marital status, severe physical or mental defects, and country of birth. Another census was made by our staff of all 8,542 colony Hutterites alive on December 31, 1950. It furnished statistics on the total membership of every colony. Detailed family records including information on age, sex, marital status, fertility, and occupation were collected for a sample of 80 per cent of the group. Hutterite family Bibles and informants were able to fill in many of the details about population movement for the seventy-year period between these two surveys.

† We undoubtedly missed some cases. In the census of 19 colonies well known to the field work staff, 1.62 per cent of the population were enumerated as deserters; there were 1.40 per cent in 65 colonies with which we had only screening contact. No person was listed as a deserter in the census reports of 9 colonies not visited by any staff member. On the other hand, a few expatriates may have been dead at the end of 1950; 51 of them, or 45 per cent, were not listed in their colony census. Most of these left twenty or more years ago. Also, some of the younger persons are likely to return after they have "tried the world" for a few years. There were 144 such "ex-deserters" at the time of our enumeration. All but three were male.

individuals. One had been institutionalized in a mental hospital for a few months; another had suffered from epilepsy and died in an asylum; a third had committed suicide. These persons were included in our case count of the mentally ill.

Many colony people were eager to impart gossip of a negative character about these deserters. In view of this prevailing attitude, the fact that only the above-mentioned three persons were known to have become major social or psychiatric problems makes it seem doubtful that those who left their colonies included a high proportion of severely disturbed cases. This conclusion was shared by nearly all officials, doctors, educators, and businessmen in areas where Hutterites live with whom this problem was discussed.

Hutterite reproduction and survival rates tend to be fairly uniform throughout the population. They show no great variations by prestige level, education, generation, or other social factors. In all other modern populations, where reproduction rates vary greatly by class, income level, education, and other social factors, allowance must be made for the extensive bias introduced by these variations. This almost complete absence of social bias in reproduction and longevity enhances the usefulness of the Hutterites for a survey of sociological factors in mental health.

Hutterites showed the highest sustained net reproduction rate (366.44) of any modern population which, to the best of our knowledge, has ever been studied. Their fertility ratio in 1950 was 96.3. At present rates, the sect will double its membership every sixteen years. Most Hutterites get married, but not particularly early in life. The median age at marriage of living women who were married during or before 1950 was 22.0; for men it was 23.5 years. There are almost no social factors which interfere with procreation after marriage. Having children is strongly supported by all cultural institutions. Husband and wife are hardly ever separated. The average completed family has over ten children. The infant death rate for 1946 to 1950 was 45 per 1,000, but generally, death rates are similar to those of the United States' white population.

In view of their high fertility and moderately low death rates, the significance of the Hutterites as a natural biosocial experiment of history may become even greater in a decade or two. Mendelian ratios for familial or possibly genetically transmitted qualities can best be estimated in large families. In many cases close to a thousand living descendants of an adult Hutterite who came to the United States from Russia would be alive in about 1966. The communal organization of the group also makes it probable that most of the people would be accessible for study.

The Hutterite population growth during the last 70 years resembles the statistical model of a *stable* population. Such a population must be distinguished from a *stationary* population. The latter is neither growing nor decreasing; it remains, as the term indicates, stationary in size. A stable population may be growing or decreasing, but it has a constant net reproduction rate. The true birth and death rates are stable. The total number of persons can change, but the percentage distribution by age and sex does not. The statistical model of a stable population has never, to our knowledge, been found in nature. The Hutterites come very close to showing its characteristics.

This finding is more than a statistical curiosity. It indicates that it is meaningful to compare the rates of phenomena, such as mental disorders, within the sect at different times, because the composition of the population base remains the same. Within the Hutterite population even crude rates can be a basis for comparison over a span of time.

Reputation for Mental Health

The Hutterite people were selected for this study because of their reputation for "peace of mind." This quality has been ascribed to them by a number of professional people who have published reports on their way of life. Bertha W. Clark,[22] who studied economics under Professor (now Senator) Paul Douglas at the University of Chicago, traveled among them in the 1920's. She reported that the sect was entirely free of crime, and she noted a general contentment with life. Lee Emerson Deets,[23] whose Doctor's thesis in sociology at Columbia University dealt with the Hutterites, observed that "insanity is almost nonexistent," and concluded that "Compared with our society, the Hutterite community is an island of certainty and security in a river of change." A report to the Manitoba legislature by the Manitoba Civil Liberties Association stated that the Hutterites do not ". . . contribute to the overcrowding of our mental hospitals since the mental security derived from their system results in a complete absence of mental illness."[24] Our own inquiry and correspondence with a large number of public officials and several scholars of Hutterite culture* supported the impression of one of the correspondents, Miss Marie Waldner. This social science teacher at Freeman College, a Mennonite school in South Dakota close to one of the centers of Hutterite settlement, stated: "Most observers credit them with remarkable mental health and usually credit it to the freedom from tension and conflict which they enjoy in their way of life."[25] In an opinion survey of 55 non-Hutterite doctors consulted by the Hutterites, the members of the sect were rated as manifesting fewer psychosomatic symptoms than their neighbors of other faiths.

---

* Dr. A. J. F. Zieglschmid, who edited the Hutterite historical manuscripts and who, at the time of his death was Professor of German at the University of Akron; Dr. Robert Friedmann, an expert on Mennonite history, now at Western Michigan College; Dr. Marcus Bach, Professor of Religion at the University of Iowa, who lived among the Hutterites for short periods and wrote a novel based on his impressions (*The Dream Gate*, New York: The Bobbs-Merrill Co., 1949); and Dr. Saul M. Katz, U. S. Department of Agriculture, who wrote a Master's thesis at Cornell University dealing with "The Security of Co-operative Farming."

The Hutterite reputation for possessing an unusual degree of "peace of mind" is of long standing. There is a report published in 1669 by a novelist, Hans Jacob Christoph Grimmelshausen, about their community life. Their contentment attracted him greatly despite the "heretical opinions contrary to the general principles of the Christian Church," which he, as a devout Catholic, believed them to entertain:

There was no anger, no jealousy, no vengeful spirit, no envy, no enmity, no concern about temporal things, no pride, no vanity, no gambling, no remorse; in a word, there was throughout and altogether a lovely harmony.[26]

The Hutterites themselves do not regard their way of life as utopian; they view it as a "narrow path" of religious restrictions. It is believed to lead to eternal salvation for those who have the self-discipline to stay within its boundaries. Hutterites live a simple life. They report among their rewards a freedom from certain "worldly worries," such as personal finances, family conflicts, and social isolation. They claim, however, no immunity from a troubled soul.

3.

Mental Disorders among the Hutterites

———————————————

THE first phase of this investigation in 1950 was focussed on how mental health is supported by sociological factors. The staff devoted much time to the study of more or less normal persons. We wanted to know how their culture supports or burdens them in meeting the problems that living brings to every human being. We asked ourselves: How are crucial life situations handled which, in the American culture, have been particularly disturbing to mentally ill individuals? For example: How are interpersonal conflicts resolved; what happens to ambition and competition; how do people adjust to misfortune, illness, old age, and the prospect of death; what is the nature of marital and sexual relationships? In other words, we started out to make a culture-personality study designed to answer this broad question: Have the Hutterites found a fountain of mental health in what one of their observers has described as a social system of high contentment?[27]

Provision for an intensive case count of mental pathology was made in a sample of the sect. Throughout our field work we were impressed with the prevailing overt atmosphere of relaxation, and absence of severe overt anxiety. Yet our sample showed more cases with serious psychiatric problems than seemed consistent with the Hutterite reputation for mental health. We then decided to check this trend of mental pathology by extending the case finding survey to the entire sect. Mental diseases are relatively rare phenomena. Frequency studies must have a large population base if they are to

Table 2—Lifetime, Active Case, and Recovery Morbidity Count of Mental Disorders Among Ethnic Hutterites Living in Summer of 1951*

Staff Diagnosis of Illness	LIFETIME MORBIDITY	ACTIVE CASE MORBIDITY		OTHER CASES	
	Total Number Ever Ill	Ill in Summer 1951	Ill but Improved on Aug. 31, 1951	Recovered by or before Aug. 31, 1951	Status Unknown
PSYCHOSES					
Schizophrenia	9	7	1	1	0
Manic-Depressive					
Reaction	39	3	5	27	4
Acute & Chronic					
Brain Disorders	5	4	0	1	0
Total	53	14	6	29	4
NEUROSES					
Psychoneurotic					
Disorders	53	24	15	12	2
Psychophysiological					
Autonomic and					
Visceral Disorders	16	7	3	5	1
Total	69	31	18	17	3
MENTAL DEFICIENCY					
Mild	14	14	0	0	0
Moderate	23	23	0	0	0
Severe	14	14	0	0	0
Total	51	51	0	0	0
EPILEPSY	20	12	5	3	0
PERSONALITY DISORDERS	6	6	0	0	0
TOTAL NUMBER OF CASES	199	114	29	49	7

* The population was 8,542 on December 31, 1950. The classification of illnesses follows the system of the committee on Nomenclature and Statistics of the American Psychiatric Association, *Diagnostic and Statistical Manual, Mental Disorders* (Washington, D.C.: American Psychiatric Association, 1952).

include enough cases to have some degree of statistical significance.

In the summer of 1951, 199 living persons, one of every 43 living Hutterites, were found who had had at one time in their life symptoms diagnosed by our staff as those of a mental disorder. About 57 per cent of these were actively ill on August 31, 1951. Roughly 15 per cent were ill but improved. Twenty-five per cent were recovered. In about 3 per cent of the cases the investigators were unable to make a judgment concerning the recovery status (see Table 2). This study did not, therefore, confirm the Hutterite reputation of virtual immunity from mental disorders.

Frequency or epidemiological surveys are based on what might be called *enumerated* morbidity (disease) counts. Their results are most meaningful for basic research when they approximate the *true* count that would be obtained if no cases were missed in the census. This quest is almost as hopeless as the effort of an absent-minded professor to count his students by asking: "Who is absent today? Please raise your hand!" Conclusive evidence concerning the true lifetime morbidity rate of mental disorders could be obtained only with vast financial resources and staff sufficient to make a thorough examination of each person in a population, and a willingness on the part of all individuals to co-operate in such an undertaking. None of the known epidemiological studies of mental disorders meet these conditions. But there are methods of estimating the elusive true rates through circumstantial evidence. The remainder of this chapter will be devoted to certain major methodological details of the detective work involved.

In several population surveys of mental disorders, different subgroups were studied with varying degrees of intensity. The Hutterites are one of the groups to which this generalization applies. The rate of the most intensively studied segment can be taken as a minimum estimate of the true rate,

Table 3—Number of Active and Recovered Cases of Mental Disorder Diagnosed in the Ethnic Population of Hutterite Colonies by Type of Staff Contact

(Rates per 1,000 in parentheses)

Type of Staff Contact	Total Population and Percentage	Psychosis	Neurosis	Mental Deficiency	Epilepsy	Personality Disorder	Total
Type I: 19 colonies screened intensively	1,671 (19%)	7 (4.2)	23 (13.8)	12 (7.2)	2 (1.2)	5 (3.0)	49 (29.3)
Type II: 65 colonies screened, with brief visiting	6,123 (72%)	45 (7.4)	44 (7.2)	36 (5.9)	15 (2.4)	1 (0.2)	141 (23.0)
Type III: 9 colonies screened through informants but never visited by staff	748 (9%)	1 (1.3)	2 (2.7)	3 (4.0)	3 (4.0)	0 (0)	9 (12.0)
Total	8,542 (100%)	53 (6.2)	69 (8.1)	51 (6.0)	20 (2.3)	6 (0.7)	199 (23.3)
Chi Square		$X^2 = 5.424$	$X^2 = 10.944$	$X^2 = .680$	$X^2 = 1.574$	$X^2 = 6.535$	$X^2 = 6.507$
Probability		$P = .07$	$P = .006$	$P = .71$	$P = .46$	$P = .04$	$P = .77$

unless there are reasons to believe that the intensively surveyed sample was not representative of the general population. We have shown in the previous chapter that the Hutterites are a highly homogeneous group, with virtually no differentiations of class, income, or standard of living. There were three categories of intensity with which their colonies were screened for the presence or absence of mentally disordered cases: I. Screening with intensive visiting; II. screening with brief visiting; and III. screening through informants only, without an on-the-spot check by the staff. (For details see Appendix on Research Procedures.) It is therefore possible to examine the mental disorder rates of the three subsamples for clues regarding the degree to which the enumerated mental disorder case count can be assumed to approximate the true morbidity count of this population.

Our findings indicate that in some categories, but not in others, the morbidity rates per 1,000 population are directly related to the intensity of field work. As Table 3 shows, the rates for psychoses show no direct relationship. The rates are highest for colonies visited briefly, lower for those studied intensively, and lowest for colonies never visited. This fact is not surprising in view of the field work techniques used in this study. Prior knowledge by the staff of the residence of most of the active psychotic patients was a major factor in determining whether a colony would or would not be visited, but it did not influence the selection of a colony for intensive study. The survey of psychoses was probably little affected by the extensive rather than intensive study of most Hutterite colonies. The absence of a direct ratio of variation between rates of psychoses and intensity of field work supports the impression of the staff that their census did not miss any case of active psychosis and few of those who had recovered from such a serious illness.

There is a direct statistically significant relationship for neuroses and personality disorders. The probability is only

6 in 1,000 that the variations in the case count of neurosis could occur by chance. For personality disorders, despite the very small number of cases in this category, the probability is 40 per 1,000. The enumeration of psychoneurotics and personality disorders is quite uneven. A number of cases are likely to have been missed in colonies not intensively enumerated. There are direct but statistically *not* significant associations of intensity of field work with the rate of mental defects and epilepsy. The case-finding process of mental defectives and epileptics appears to have been somewhat more thorough.

Similar conclusions are derived when all mental disorders are broken into two dichotomous categories:

1. "Severe" cases: those least likely to be missed in a morbidity study because the cases are actively ill and have severely disabling symptoms. "Severe" cases include all active psychoses, moderate and severe mental deficiences, and all active cases of epilepsy.

2. "Mild" cases: those most likely to be missed because the cases were not ill at the time of the survey, were improving, or were ill with symptoms which were less serious in their impairment of social or physical function. This category includes all improved and recovered cases of psychosis, all psychoneurotic patients, improved and recovered cases of epilepsy, and all persons affected by personality disorders.

We found no significant difference by intensity of coverage in the morbidity rates of "severe" cases (probability of chance occurrence 87 per cent), but the difference for mild cases was significant at the 5 per cent level.

It is logical to assume that the coverage of inactive or former psychotic patients would be less complete than that of active cases. A review of our data of the estimated onset of illness of all enumerated cases, including those who were dead on August 31, 1951, leads us to believe that there were few such cases. One might assume that the name of a patient who had had a manic-depressive episode several decades ago might easily be forgotten. However, manic-depressive cases were found to be distributed evenly over the entire period, when adjusted for the rapid increase in the Hutterite population. In 1910, for example, there were only 1,400 persons, of whom approximately 700 were adults over 15 years of age, who were potentially subject to psychoses. There were 5 living persons who had had a manic-depressive reaction; about 6 would have been expected on the basis of the 1951 Hutterite lifetime morbidity rate. The distribution of schizophrenics was not uniform. But this disorder was characterized by symptoms so well recognized by Hutterites that it is doubtful that any clear-cut case of schizophrenia would have failed to turn up in our extensive screening process. On the other hand, we are fairly certain that our informants failed to identify some of the deceased cases of senile psychoses. Their distribution over the period 1880-1951 is least convincing of completeness. No case was found who became ill before 1940. It is probable that some of the members of the Hutterite ethnic group who were feeble when they died might have been diagnosed by our staff as senile psychotic, if full information about their condition had been available.

The risk that our screening process missed a few cases of psychosis is balanced by a possibility that some of the cases diagnosed by us as "recovered" may not have been psychotic. Memories tend to become embellished with age. It is hard enough to make a good diagnosis when a patient can be observed in a hospital over a long period of time. Some of our diagnoses were made of persons with whom our staff had only a superficial and secondary contact. They involve conditions of the past as they live in the memory of nonprofessional informants.

The general validity of the case count of living psychotics

is somewhat strengthened by the similarity of estimated life-time morbidity rates for 1951 and 1930. Table 4 shows that the estimated lifetime morbidity rate in 1930 does not differ significantly from that obtained in the 1951 survey.

Table 4—Lifetime Morbidity Rates of Psychosis in the Ethnic Hutterite Population of 1951 and 1930*

Year	Total Population	Number of Cases Ever Ill in Their Life	Lifetime Morbidity Rate per 1000 Population
1951	8,542	53	6.2
1930	3,400	19	5.6
$X^2 = .069$		$P = .79$	

* The enumeration of cases was completed on August 31, 1951, but the population is based on a census as of December 31, 1950. The population figure for 1930 is an estimate. The case count includes 14 persons living in 1951 who were ill at some time before 1930, and 5 persons dead in 1951 who were living in 1930 and had been ill at or before that time.

In summary, Hutterite mental patients were found in every one of the five major diagnostic categories. Our evidence indicates that the case count of this study may be nearly complete for all psychoses, epilepsy, and mental deficiency cases with severely disabling symptoms. Psychoneurotics, persons with mild mental defects, persons with mild personality disorders, and nonpsychotic persons with a history of a past disorder were probably underenumerated.

The Hutterite way of life, despite the good mental health reputation of its members, provides no immunity from severe psychiatric disturbances. This finding calls to mind a similar one by Dorothea Leighton and Clyde Kluckhohn.[28] They made a careful psychological study of Navaho Indians and found them to show considerable emotional instability and high levels of anxiety. They contrasted these trends with the fact that Navahos are renowned, among some outsiders who think they know them, as being "stolid" or "just happy children." Certainly no generalization about the state of mental health of a group can be made without a thorough study. Appearances and impressions based on superficial contacts can be very deceiving.

The epidemiological finding that psychoses occur with regularity in a very protective and fairly well integrated social system strongly supports the theory that no culture can provide immunity from mental disorders. Psychoses are probably a universal phenomenon, but there is still the question of relative morbidity. How does the experience of the Hutterite population compare with that of other groups? The following two chapters will be specifically addressed to this problem.

4.

Comparison of
Ten Populations: Methods

THE extreme Hutterite reputation for mental health was not confirmed, but this finding leaves unanswered the question whether there is anything distinctive about the relative size of Hutterite morbidity rates and symptoms. Our data suggest that sociological factors are indeed significant. In later chapters this will be shown in discussions of specific disorders. Before proceeding to the clinical analysis of Hutterite cases and their symptoms it will be useful to see how far our findings lend themselves to cross-cultural comparison through quantitative methods. The method for comparison will be described in this chapter; in Chapter 5 the results of the comparison are presented.

During the past 25 years census-type surveys of mental disorders have been made in nine American and European populations.* The studies varied in many respects, but in each

* There is also an excellent morbidity survey by Fremming of all persons born on the Island of Bornholm between 1883 and 1887. Fremming's biographical method differs fundamentally from the census method of

an attempt was made to enumerate living persons ever known
to have been affected. Included were not only active cases
in mental hospitals, but also recovered cases and those who
were ill but never institutionalized. The published reports
are most complete for psychoses. We shall therefore restrict
our most detailed cross-cultural comparison to this category
of mental disorders. The studies include, in addition to the
Hutterite survey, Brugger's Thuringia Villages Study and
Bavarian Villages Study,[29] Strömgren's Bornholm Island
Study,[30] The 1936 Lemkau-Tietze-Cooper Study[31] of the
Eastern Health District in Baltimore,† Luten-Roth's Study
of Williamson County, Tennessee,[32] Sjögren's West Swedish
Island Study,[33] Böök's North Swedish Parishes Study,[34] and
Bremer's Arctic Village Study in Norway.[35] Shortly before
this book went to press Tsung-yi Lin reported on an appar-
ently excellent census study of three communities on the
Island of Formosa.[36] It provides a welcome opportunity to
compare Western findings with those of an Asiatic population. In 1943 Lemkau, Tietze, and Cooper compared the first
five of these studies. They concluded:

---

the other ten surveys. Their results cannot be compared. See Kurt H.
Fremming, *The Expectation of Mental Infirmity in a Sample of the Danish
Population* (London: The Eugenics Society and Cassell and Company Ltd.,
1951). There are several dozen other studies which report morbidity data
based on small samples selected mostly on a proband basis. Their findings
are not applicable to our problem. For review and a complete bibliography
see Erik Strömgren, "Statistical and Genetic Population Studies Within
Psychiatry; Methods and Principal Results," *Actualités Scientifiques et
Industrielles*, Congrès International de Psychiatrie, VI, Psychiatrie Sociale
(Paris: Herman & Cie., 1950), p. 1101.

† The Baltimore study is not fully comparable to the other nine. Its
staff concentrated only on the enumeration of patients hospitalized during
1936. The results of this survey can be made somewhat comparable to those
of the others by combining the 367 active psychotic patients and 26 patients "with psychotic traits" with 114 postpsychotic patients. They were
individuals known to have been residents in the district in 1936 who had
been psychotic at some previous time but were not known to have been
psychotic during that year. This total of 507 cases can be used as a minimum
estimate of the lifetime morbidity count of this population.

It appears that poor selection of sample populations and insufficient numbers of cases as well as differences in investigative methods, differences in diagnosis and classification tend to make available studies of prevalence and incidence *basically incomparable*.[37] [Italics ours.]

These conclusions were valid then. However, more detailed analysis has made it possible to increase the degree of comparability of these studies. Some of their variations are known, and corrections can be made for them; other sources of variation can be roughly estimated. While the residue of uncontrolled variables is still great, this process permits us to make some fruitful comparisons.

A Cumulative Approach to the Measurement of Population Morbidity

Most frequency studies of mental disorders are based on hospital and other official records of active cases. The findings are expressed as *incidence* or *prevalence* rates. *Incidence* is the number of new cases of a disease occurring within a specified period of time, most commonly a year. *Prevalence* is the number of both new and old cases of a disease present in a population group at a specified time. It is derived by taking the number of cases at the start of an interval plus the new cases developing during the interval. Both of these rates are predicated on the logical assumption that the population remains fairly stationary throughout the period under study. Since mental disorders are a relatively rare event, incidence and prevalence rates are most meaningful when they are calculated on a large population base.

The Hutterite sect and the other nine populations for which we have data are fairly small. They had to be small to be studied with some degree of intensity. The number of new mental cases in any given year in such groups is insufficient to calculate stable rates. For example, in the Hutterite sect the average incidence of new cases in the last twenty years was only about 2½ new cases per year. In order to compensate for the rareness of new cases during the actual period of field investigation, our study had to adopt a cumulative method by extending the range of the study over the longest possible time interval for which data could be obtained with some expectation of approximate completeness. This was the entire lifetime of all Hutterites recorded as born into a colony and alive on December 31, 1950. This approach can answer the following question:

What has been the experience of the population with mental disorders throughout the lifetime of all those living on a particular date?

The time dimension for enumerating cases was the cumulative life span of all persons alive on the survey date. The following morbidity measures were found to be useful:

1. Active Case Morbidity
2. Recovered Case Morbidity
3. Enumerated Lifetime Morbidity
4. True Lifetime Morbidity
5. Hospitalization Ratio
6. Recovery Ratio

These measures are defined and illustrated in Table 5. Their similarities and differences from the conventional incidence and prevalence concepts are also shown. Lifetime morbidity measures describe past experience and, in a stable population, can also be used to estimate future morbidity rates. As was indicated previously, this model does not fit most populations, but it does fit the Hutterites fairly well. Despite their rapid increase, their age and sex distribution has been fairly stable. In such a group lifetime morbidity rates can be used to make predictions for the future on the usual logical qualification that all other factors remain unchanged.

Table 5—Seven Measures of Morbidity Applied to the Hutterite Data

Morbidity Measure	Definition	Time Period Covered	Illustrations Using the Findings of Psychoses of the Hutterite Study
Incidence	All new cases during the enumeration period, including persons living and dead at the end of the period.	Specific beginning and ending dates of enumeration.	About $2\frac{1}{2}$ cases per year or 0.86 per 1,000 age 15 and over, during the period January 1, 1930 to August 31, 1951.
Active Case Morbidity (similar to Prevalence)	All active cases alive at the end of the period.	Definite end-date of enumeration; open-ended beginning (in prevalence a definite beginning for the interval of observation should be specified).	20 living active cases in August 31, 1951, or 4.7 per 1,000 age 15 and over.
Recovered Case Morbidity	All living cases ill at one time of their life but recovered at the end of the enumeration period.	Definite end-date of enumeration; open-ended beginning.	29 living cases recovered by August 31, 1951, or 6.9 per 1,000 age 15 and over. Recovery status is not clear for 4 other cases, 1.0 cases per 1,000 age 15 and over. They are probably not active cases.
Enumerated Lifetime Morbidity	All active and recovered cases alive at the end of the enumeration period. The sum of active and recovered case morbidity.	Definite end-date of enumeration; open-ended beginning.	53 living cases ever ill in their life on or before August 31, 1951, or 12.6 per 1,000 age 15 and over.
True Lifetime Morbidity	An estimate of true morbidity: active and recovered cases alive at the end of the period, including those estimated to have been missed in the enumeration process.	Definite end-date of enumeration; open-ended beginning.	About 13 cases per 1,000 age 15 and over. Probably close to enumerated lifetime morbidity rate.
Hospitalization Ratio	Number of living active or recovered cases ever hospitalized as mental patients. $$\frac{\text{Enumerated Lifetime morbidity.}}{}$$	Definite end-date of enumeration; open-ended beginning.	$\dfrac{4}{53} = 7.5\%$
Recovery Ratio	Recovered cases. Enumerated lifetime morbidity.	Definite end-date of enumeration; open-ended beginning.	$\dfrac{29}{53} = 54.7\%$

The Standard Expectancy Method

Mental disorder rates often are tabulated on the basis of crude rates per 1,000 or 100,000. For example, in the United States in 1948 there were aproximately 3.8 persons per 1,000 in a mental hospital.[38] Of 4,130 persons born on the island of Bornholm between 1883 and 1887 who could be traced by investigators and who lived beyond the tenth year of life, 42 persons per 1,000 were found to have been psychotic at some time during their life before their 56th birthday or their death, whichever occurred earlier.[39] Of 8,542 Hutterites living in 1950, 6.1 per 1,000 were diagnosed as having shown symptoms of psychosis at some time during their life up to that time. On the surface these crude rates seem to have some basis for comparability. All are *rates per 1,000 persons.* Actually crude rates are very misleading. The three examples cited have different criteria for case counting. The United States rate is based only on persons in a mental hospital at the end of 1948. Fremming's study of Bornholm counted living and dead psychotics who were born between 1883 and 1887. Thirty per cent of the 79 cases diagnosed by him as schizophrenic or manic-depressive were never in a mental hospital. The Hutterite study counted all cases living in 1951 regardless of their date of birth. Few were ever in a mental hospital.

Crude rates are not necessarily comparable even when the same criterion for case counting was used. This fact is well illustrated in Table 6, comparing three quite similar studies which counted all living persons ever ill with a mental disorder. Although the Hutterite, the North Swedish Area, and the West Swedish Island populations are rural and of approximately the same size, they differ greatly in age and sex distribution. The Hutterites are predominantly young; the inhabitants of the West Swedish Island are predominantly old. The North Swedish area people have an age distribution somewhere between these two extremes, with an unusual excess of males over females. Since most mental disorders are age-correlated and some are sex-correlated, crude morbidity rates are obviously a poor index of a group's experience with mental disorders.

Table 6—Comparative Age and Sex Distribution of the Population of Ethnic Hutterite Colonies, North Swedish Area and the West Swedish Island, and Their Relationships to Crude Rates of Psychosis

Area	Total Population	Percentage of Population under 15	Percentage of Population over 60	Sex Ratio Total Population	Crude Rate of Psychosis*
Ethnic Hutterites	8,542	50.6	2.6	1.00	6.2
North Swedish Area	8,651	41.6	7.3	1.14	12.4
West Swedish Island	8,735	22.0	16.9	1.04	10.8

* Per 1000 population.

Corrections for age and sex distribution variations, therefore, are a minimum prerequisite to achieve greater comparability. In many previous studies this was attempted through the application of the *Abridged Method of Weinberg*.[40] The method has been favored by European scholars who were genetically oriented and were looking for genetic evidence related to specific diagnostic categories. The Weinberg formula involves the use of a somewhat arbitrary "risk period" for each specific diagnostic category, such as schizophrenia, manic-depressive reaction, or senile psychosis. This method is of questionable validity because variations of diagnostic standards and terminology in the different studies are great, and because the age distribution of persons within the risk period is not taken into account.

Our comparison is based on the total number of all psychoses. This grouping reduces the variance introduced by the differences in diagnostic standards of the several investigators. In place of the Weinberg formula, we use what may be termed the *Standard Expectancy Method*. The age-sex specific rates for *all* psychoses of one population are selected as a standard. The rates of this *standard population* are then

applied as weights to each of the other groups. The number
of persons in each age and sex category is multiplied by the
apropriate age-sex specific morbidity rate of the standard
population. This calculation furnishes an *expected* frequency
of psychoses for each group—expected if its members were
subject to mental disorders at the rates of the standard population. The *actual* number of mental disorder cases in each
group can then be expressed as a ratio of the expected number. This *Expectancy Ratio* shows how far the populations
deviate from the standard population in their frequency of
mental disorders. All denominators are calculated on the
morbidity experience of the same standard population. The
Expectancy Ratios show the refined quantitative differences
that remain after eliminating those due to variations in age
and sex distribution.

$$\frac{\text{Actual number of cases found}}{\text{Expected number of cases on the basis of the standard rates}} \text{ or } \frac{a}{e}$$

The standard expectancy method can be used with any
population serving as a standard. We shall compare the ten
studies by weighing them with Hutterite lifetime morbidity
rates, which are given in Table 7. Unfortunately, these rates
are not very stable because they are based on a small number
of cases in each age-sex category. More stable rates would be

Table 7—Age Specific Lifetime Morbidity Rates of Psychosis of Ethnic Hutterites on About August 31, 1951

AGE	POPULATION		NUMBER EVER AFFECTED BY A PSYCHOSIS		RATE PER 1,000 PERSONS	
	Male	Female	Male	Female	Male	Female
0-14	2,190	2,134	0	0	0.0	0.0
15-29	1,062	1,115	2	3	1.9	2.7
30-44	585	564	5	7	8.5	12.4
45-59	290	271	12	10	41.4	36.9
60 & over	120	105	4	10	33.3	95.2
Total	4,274*	4,189*	23	30	5.4	7.2

* The total ethnic Hutterite population is 8,542. Excluded from these totals are 34 males and 72 females whose ages are unknown.. . .

preferable as a standard for comparison. Conditional expectancy rates have been calculated by Goldhamer and Marshall for hospitalized patients, on the basis of first admission rates to mental hospitals in New York State in 1940. These rates are only *approximately* comparable to the lifetime morbidity rates of this study. However, the advantages of stability, because the Goldhamer-Marshall data are based on a population of almost 13½ million, outweigh the minor errors which arises from differences in methods of calculating lifetime morbidity and conditional expectancy rates. Lifetime morbidity rates represent the past experience of a population with mental disorders, without considering those who died before the study was made. Conditional expectancy rates represent the future number of chances out of 100 that a person of any given age in New York State in 1940 will be admitted to a mental hospital for the first time before he reaches a given later age. Here, too, persons who die before reaching this age are not considered in the calculations.

The Goldhamer-Marshall conditional expectancy rates have been calculated for five-year age ranges. The rates are based only on patients hospitalized for the first time in New York State in 1940. They exclude psychotic individuals who do not get into a mental hospital. New York State hospital rates, however, can be presumed to include a larger proportion of all truly psychotic cases than the rates of most other large political subdivisions. New York State has fairly good diagnostic facilities for mental cases. It is a predominantly urban state, where mental patients cannot easily be cared for at home or by friends without coming to the attention of medical or governmental agencies. Although New York State hospital rates of psychotics are far from being a measure of true morbidity, they probably approximate this measure more than the hospital rates of any other area for which fairly stable rates, broken down by age and sex, are available.

The standard procedures of the Standard Expectancy

Method are illustrated with the Hutterite population in Table 8. The number of persons in every five-year age group is multiplied by the conditional expectancy rate that would apply if those involved lived in New York State in 1940 and were within the group which had reached the midpoint of their age group.

Table 8—*Tabulation of the Number of Psychotics Expected in a Population Equal to the Hutterites in Age and Sex Distribution on the Basis of the Goldhamer-Marshall Conditional Expectancy Rates for New York State—1940**

AGE	HUTTERITE POPULATION†		MIDPOINT IN AGE GROUP	NEW YORK STATE CONDITIONAL EXPECTANCY RATE ESTIMATED FOR MIDPOINT OF COHORT		NUMBER OF PSY-CHOTICS EXPECTED TO HAVE BECOME HOSPITALIZED IN EACH COHORT	
	Male	Female		Male	Female	Male	Female
Under 14	2,190	2,134	7.5	.1	.1	2	2
15-19	434	474	17.5	.2	.2	1	1
20-24	330	337	22.5	.6	.5	2	2
25-29	298	304	27.5	1.2	1.0	4	3
30-34	231	231	32.5	1.8	1.5	4	3
35-39	189	213	37.5	2.4	2.1	5	4
40-44	165	120	42.5	3.1	2.7	5	3
45-49	125	111	47.5	3.9	3.4	5	4
50-54	91	91	52.5	4.8	4.2	4	4
55-59	74	69	57.5	5.6	4.8	4	3
60-64	46	40	62.5	6.5	5.7	3	2
65-69	39	25	67.5	7.8	6.8	3	2
70-74	22	29	72.5	9.5	8.3	2	2
75-79	5	6	77.5	11.9	10.5	1	1
80-84	5	3	82.5	15.5	13.5	1	1
85-89	3	1	87.5	20.0	17.7	1	0
90 & Over	0	2	90.0	21.4	19.9	0	0
Unknown	34	72		1.0	1.0	0	1
Total	4,281	4,261				47	38

* Herbert Goldhamer and Andrew W. Marshall, *Psychosis and Civilization* (Glencoe, Illinois: The Free Press, 1953) pp. 114-115.
† The figures within each age range are based on the enumeration of 80% of the population by single years of age and the enumeration of the remaining 20% in broader age groups. The latter were distributed within the different age and sex groups in the same proportion as the 80% sample, for which full information is available.

1. Staff Orientation

The Standard Expectancy Method has many limitations. It can correct only for differences in age and sex distribution.

There are other important variables in the population studies. Published reports often do not contain enough data even to estimate their effect on the over-all results. But there is some information on six of these variables which can be utilized in comparative analysis. The ten surveys are the work of ten "nonstandardized" groups of scholars. Five of the European studies had a genetic orientation. The three American, the Formosan, and the Arctic Norwegian Village studies paid little attention to genetic factors; they focussed on the social-psychiatric and public health implications of morbidity rates. There were great variations in the amount and type of attention that could be devoted to the individual cases and to the entire study. Medically trained personnel actively participated in all studies, but some studies did not have adequate support from persons skilled in handling the social-anthropological and statistical aspects.

2. DIAGNOSTIC STANDARDS

Diagnostic labels in psychiatry are still far from being standardized either conceptually or in application. As Ernest Gruenberg points out in a review of major mental disorders, ". . . there is in general, I find in going over the literature, a great deal of skepticism regarding the validity of diagnosis in the phychoses."[41] This point is also made by Ödegaard in his study of *Emigration and Insanity*:[42]

Diagnoses in psychiatry vary not only from one generation of psychiatrists to another, but even from one hospital to another. Hardly two psychiatrists can be found who would agree as to the differential diagnosis between "schizophrenia" and "manic-depressive" insanity.

Ödegaard is perhaps overly pessimistic with regard to the possibility for some general agreement among psychiatrists of the *same* school of thought, but the ten surveys generally support his views. This fact is shown in Table 9, which shows the extent of variation in the relative proportions of major diagnostic groups.

Table 9—Major Diagnostic Categories in Ten Studies of Psychosis

		PERCENTAGE OF CASES DIAGNOSED			
Study	Number of Cases Diagnosed	Schizo-phrenia	Manic Depression	All Other Diagnoses	Total
Ethnic Hutterites	53	17	74	9	100
Formosa Area	76	57	17	26	100
North Swedish Area	107	87	2	11	100
Arctic Norwegian Village	38	16	5	79	100
West Swedish Island	94	43	27	30	100
Bornholm Island	481	31	25	43	100
Williamson County, Tennessee	156	27	26	47	100
Baltimore Eastern Health District	367*	43	11	46	100
Thuringia Villages	200	37	10	53	100
Bavarian Villages, Rosenheim Area	21	38	10	52	100

* Active and severe cases only. Recovered cases are not included, as no diagnostic break-down is given for them.

The proportion of schizophrenics varies from a low of 16 per cent in the Arctic Norwegian Village to a high of 87 per cent in the North Swedish Area; the proportion of manic-depressives from a low of 2 per cent in the North Swedish Area to 74 per cent in the Hutterite group. All other diagnostic categories, including cases not diagnosed, vary from a low of 9 per cent in the Hutterite study of 79 per cent in the Arctic Norwegian Village survey.

Probably there are some real differences in the distribution of psychotic symptoms in these populations. We suspect, however, that variations of psychiatric training of the respective research staffs are also a major factor. For example, most of the European reports include epileptics in their case count of psychotics; the American do not. We corrected for this discrepancy by eliminating epileptics from all tabulations, except where there was evidence that the patient suffered from epilepsy with psychosis. Alcoholics, psychopaths, and character disorder cases appear to have been included more freely among those enumerated as psychotic in the European surveys than in the American and Chinese investigations. In six of the studies, from 5 to 8 per cent of the psychotic cases are left "undiagnosed." In the Hutterite study, and apparently in others, the policy was to diagnose every case on the assumption that a tentative judgment in difficult cases is preferable. In the light of the magnitude of these variations in the use of diagnostic categories, the Weinberg method of comparison by specific diagnoses seems less suitable for cross-cultural comparison than the Standard Expectancy Method.

3. DEATH RATES

Psychoses are most prevalent in the older age groups. This fact may account for the report of some anthropologists that diseases are rare in the cultures which they have studied. The life expectancy of most primitive groups is quite low. Many people do not live long enough to go through the risk period for many of the psychoses. However, differences in longevity are a relatively small source of variance in most of the studies under review. The Formosa report constitutes a significant exception to this generalization. The age specific death rates for young and middle-aged adults on this Chinese island in 1950 were generally much more than twice as high as in the American and European countries where epidemiological census studies have been made. In general, the death rates were lowest in Norway, with Sweden, Denmark, Germany, and the United States following closely in that order.[43]

4. MIGRATION

Selective migration might be a major source of variance between the populations that have been studied. It will be recalled from Chapter 2 that among the Hutterites in- and out-migration were very small. The Formosa study was limited to Chinese born in Formosa. Dr. Tsung-yi Lin's report does not contain any information about intra-island migration of the survey population, but he states that "population movements were not a factor" in his investigation. In all other groups there was considerable migration, and it may have been psychiatrically selective.*

5. ENUMERATION CRITERION

Permanent residence in the survey area at the time of the study was the criterion for including persons in seven of the surveys. Patients who were born in the area but left it were not counted unless they became ill while residing in the area and were hospitalized from there. The same procedure was used in the West Swedish Island, the North Swedish Area, and the Hutterite sect. All mental patients resident in these areas were enumerated; in addition, excellent records of pop-

---

* In Thuringia 28 per cent of the population was born outside the area. In the Bavarian villages 44 per cent were in-migrants. In the Arctic Norwegian Village 47 per cent of the population was not born there; most of the natives were children of parents who earlier had chosen to migrate to this forlorn region. The crude rate of all mental disorders of persons born in the village was only 59 per cent as high as the rate of persons who migrated there. Data on out-migration for these areas is not available. In the West Swedish Island there was considerable out-migration during the forty-year span covered by the study. The island had a population of 10,352 persons on January 1, 1900. In 1944, despite an excess of births over deaths, it had shrunk by almost 16 per cent to 8,736 inhabitants. Dr. Sjögren enumerated 109 psychotic patients who were born on the island and were known to be living. However, only 94 of these individuals were still resident on the island on December 31, 1944. In addition there were 14 patients who disappeared from sight. Most of these people were probably alive in 1944. In other words, between 15 and 29 cases were probably lost to the study through migration and disappearance from sight, a number equal to 16-31 per cent of the 1944 lifetime case count of 94 persons. Circumstantial evidence also suggests that there was a good deal of in- or out-migration in the North Swedish Area. The sex ratio of its population was 1.14. Such a predominance of males over females is hardly possible through an excess of male births. The explanation lies either in a heavy in-migration of males or an out-migration of females. The deficiency of females (or excess of males) is particularly high in the age groups of 20-29, 35-49, and 60-64, which have a sex ratio in excess of 1.30—more than 130 males to every 100 females.

ulation movement were available, which made it possible to enumerate mental patients who were born in the survey area but had migrated from it to other parts of the country before they became ill. In these three studies it was possible, therefore, to estimate some of the effect of poulation mobility or morbidity rates. The statistics of all ten studies have been calculated with the same criterion of inclusiveness to achieve maximum comparability. Only living persons permanently resident in the areas at the completion of each study were counted.*

6. COMPLETENESS OF COVERAGE

There is no certain way of knowing how many cases were missed in any of the studies. Estimates of true morbidity rates can be made to some extent through the use of three indexes:

I. Association of morbidity rates and intensity of field work.

II. The hospitalization ratio:

$$\frac{h}{a} = \frac{\text{Number of cases ever hospitalized}}{\text{Actual number of cases enumerated}}$$

III. The recovery ratio:

$$\frac{r}{a} = \frac{\text{Number of cases known to have recovered}}{\text{Actual number of cases enumerated}}$$

I.

In the Hutterite study, as was demonstrated in the previous chapter, the intensity of survey methods was not directly related to the rates of psychoses. If we can assume that psychoses are randomly distributed throughout this very homo-

---

* We have made a slight exception in the Hutterite study. All living ethnic Hutterites were counted. One probably recovered psychotic patient who had broken with his community in 1951 was therefore included in our case count of 53 living patients.

geneous religious sect, it is reasonable to conclude that the extensive screening methods used for most of the population were as productive for locating psychotic patients as were the more intensive survey methods used in nineteen of the colonies.

In the Formosa study no significant differences were noted in the over-all rate of mental disorders between three different sections of the island. One of them was a small rural village, the other a section of a town of 20,000 population, and the third a district in a modern port city with 120,000 inhabitants. Each of these three areas was screened with the same methods and the same degree of intensity. The absence of rural-urban differences in mental disorder rates, which are generally found in American and European countries, is noteworthy. The uniformity of morbidity rates within the population may mean that the exposure to the risk of becoming mentally ill is fairly uniform throughout the Formosa population. It is also possible that the extensive screening methods employed by Dr. Tsung-yi Lin and his staff were effective in locating all active or recovered cases of psychosis in the rural area, but less effective in the urban areas. The urban officials who helped in the "case hunt" may well have had less intimate knowledge of their population.

In three other studies the published reports include information which indicates that the frequency of psychoses was significantly higher for areas or groups that were studied intensively than for areas or groups that were screened less thoroughly. In Williamson County, Tennessee, ". . . the case rate [of all forms of mental disability, not merely of psychosis] for these three civil districts which are included in the intensive survey areas was 123.7 per 1,000. The case rate for the remainder of the county was 64.5 per 1,000."[44] On Bornholm Island, Strömgren carried out a very intensive survey of one village with 913 inhabitants. The lifetime psychosis rate per 1,000 persons aged 15 or over in this admittedly very small group was about 36 per cent higher than it was in the population of the entire island. Sjögren reported evidence that the enumeration of recent cases on the West Swedish Island was more complete than the case count of early years. In Sweden the law requires the official registration of all mental patients both inside and outside of mental hospitals. Of the early psychotic cases who died before December 31, 1944, 86 per cent were officially registered, whereas 47 per cent of the living patients were not registered. Sjögren believes that the enumeration of a larger proportion of nonregistered patients among the living cases was largely due to the underenumeration of nonregistered types among the dead patients. His conclusions probably apply to many of the other studies:

Despite thorough field and familial investigation carried out, we must make allowance for the fact that there are certainly several primarily mild cases of mental disease and abnormality which have not been registered. The patients themselves and their relations certainly not infrequently conceal mild cases of, for example, manic-depressive psychosis, psychogenic reactions, alcoholism, etc., particularly if they occurred some time previously. Nor are mild clinical pictures of presenile, senile and arteriosclerotic psychoses easy to reveal in field investigations. Numerous cases of epilepsy are certainly never reported owing, *inter alia*, to the fact that in Sweden marriage has been forbidden in cases of endogenous epilepsy.[45]

II.

The ratio of hospitalized cases to all enumerated patients may also reflect the completeness of the enumeration process. Variations in the hospitalization ratio can be only partly a function of the extent to which the researchers had access to persons with milder psychotic conditions. Some variations in the ratios are to be expected because there are important differences in social practice regarding hospitalization in the areas studied. In Williamson County, Tennessee, the Balti-

more Eastern Health District, Bornholm Island, the Thuringia Villages, and the North Swedish Area, between 75 and
85 per cent of the cases had been in a hospital at some time.
These high hospitalization rates raise a serious question about
the effectiveness of the screening procedures employed for
locating milder and nonhospitalized cases of psychoses. These
doubts are strengthened if one notes the lower hospitalization
ratios of other studies where treatment facilities available were
similar to those of the areas where four out of five enumerated patients received hospital care. On Formosa only 60 per
cent of the enumerated cases were known to hospitals or to
local practicing physicians. In the Arctic Norwegian Village
55 per cent of the cases were treated in a hospital for their
mental condition. In the West Swedish Island the hospitalization ratio was 34 per cent. Among the Hutterites the rate was
only 8 per cent. To the extent that the hospitalization ratio
is a criterion of the completeness of the enumeration process,
the Hutterite survey appears to have been relatively thorough.

III.

In many families past mental illnesses are not readily discussed by those who know about them. For this and other
reasons, recovered cases are more easily missed than active
cases. At least 55 per cent of the enumerated Hutterite patients had fully recovered when the survey was made. About
50 per cent of the cases were transitory and mild in the
Arctic Norwegan Village. In the West Swedish Island 38
per cent of the enumerated cases were inactive. This proportion was 22 per cent in the Tennessee County. In the North
Swedish Area 13 per cent of the patients had completely
recovered and were able to work; another 24 per cent seemed
recovered and were able to work to some extent. No comparable data on recovery are available for the other five
studies. The Hutterites thus have the highest ratio of recovered patients among those for which we have data. It is pos-

sible that more patients recover in some groups than in others. However, it is also likely that at least some of these recovery ratio differences reflect the degree of completness of the screening process, although among the Hutterites a high recovery rate could also be partly ascribed to the high frequency of depressive psychoses, which generally have a good prognosis for recovery.

All of these partial indexes of completeness of coverage can be measured with some degree of reliability. Association of morbidity rates with field work intensity can be checked accurately if each case is classified by its place of enumeration. The hospitalization ratio is based on a criterion which is usually a matter of public record—presence or absence on the rolls of a mental hospital. The recovery ratio is perhaps the least reliable of the three indexes, but it is probably significant that the Hutterite rates reflect relatively effective screening procedures on the basis of all three indexes.

5.

Comparison of
Ten Populations: Results

The Frequency of Psychoses

WE ARE now ready to proceed to a rank ordering of the lifetime morbidity data on psychoses of the ten studies. The Standard Expectancy Method was used to make adjustments for population differences in age and sex distribution. Both the Hutterite and the New York State expectancy rates were applied as norms for making the adjustments.

The rank order of morbidity of the populations varies little, irrespective of the rates used as norms in the Standard Expectancy Method calculations. The Hutterite sect ranks third. The Arctic Norwegian Village has the highest frequency of psychoses, almost twice the Hutterite rate, with the North Swedish Area taking second place. Both of these recent Scandinavian investigations, judging from their published reports, were quite thorough in their screening process. All of the three top-ranking populations are rural and culturally isolated. In the two Scandinavian populations, however, selective

Table 10—Comparison of Ten Lifetime Morbidity Surveys of Psychoses by the Standard Expectancy Method

		a Actual Number of Cases Found	e EXPECTED NUMBER OF CASES		$\frac{a}{e}$ EXPECTANCY RATIOS	
Survey	Total Population		Hutterite Norms	N. Y. State Norms	Hutterite Norms	N. Y. State Norms
Arctic Norwegian Village	1,325	38	19	26	1.97	1.43.
North Swedish Area	8,651	107	94	141	1.14	.76
Ethnic Hutterites	8,542	53	53	85	1.00	.62
Bornholm Island*	45,694	481	773	1,049	.62	.46
Baltimore Eastern Health District†	55,129	507	822	1,144	.62	.44
Williamson County, Tennessee‡	24,804	156	271	502	.58	.31
West Swedish Island	8,735	94	186	260	.51	.36
Bavarian Villages, Rosenheim Area	3,203	21	49	84	.43	.25
Formosa Area	19,913	76	194	273	.39	.28
Thuringia Villages	37,546	200	617	841	.32	.24

* Age and sex distribution of population as of May 11, 1930.

† The population of the Baltimore Eastern Health District was 55,129 in 1936. No age and sex distribution for this population is given in the published reports of the study. In 1940 the total population of the district, which included Wards 6 and 7 in Baltimore, was 61,617. The number of expected cases for 1936 was tabulated on the assumption that the age and sex distribution in 1936 and 1940 did not change significantly. Lemkau, Tietze, and Cooper also made this assumption in adjusting different population estimates to each other. See Paul Lemkau, Christopher Tietze, and Marcia Cooper, ''Mental Hygiene Problems in an Urban District,'' *Mental Hygiene*, Vol. XXVI, No. 1 (January, 1942), pp. 100-119.

‡ The population as of September 1, 1938. The age and sex distribution is that of the 1940 United States census, because no such breakdown is contained in the published report for 1938.

migration may have been a major factor. Persons who are socially marginal are more likely to settle or migrate there than socially well adjusted people.

The Hutterites have a higher *enumerated* rate of psychoses than seven of the ten populations. One possible interpretation is that the sect has a relatively large proportion of members who are prone to become ill with a psychosis. This explanation, however, does not seem logical in the light of our clinical and social-anthropological observations. Could the true frequency of psychoses among the Hutterites be almost a third more frequent than among the dwellers in the Baltimore Eastern Health District, most of which is a slum area, with all the evidence of social disorganization commonly found in such an urban section?

We are more inclined to accept the theory that the relatively high rank of the Hutterite expectancy ratio is a function of the thoroughness of the survey methods. As was indicated in the previous chapter, there is considerable evidence to question the effectiveness of enumeration in at last five of the seven studies which rank below the Hutterites in their morbidity rates. The Bornholm Island, the Baltimore Eastern Health District, the Bavarian Villages, and the Thuringia Villages studies were poorly screened for mental patients who had recovered from their illness and those whose symptoms were mild and who were outside of mental hospitals. It is very probable that the size and relative rank of their true morbidity rates of psychoses would be considerably higher than is indicated by their expectancy ratios.

The Arctic Norwegian Village, North Swedish Area, Hutterite, West Swedish Island, and Formosa Area studies are in a different category of reliability. All of them were made within the last decade. Their reports show considerable awareness of the technical problems involved in the effort to achieve a complete enumeration of cases necessary to calculate lifetime morbidity rates. There were, without doubt, major differences in the orientation of their staff, the diagnostic standards, and other factors, for which no estimate of quantitative effects on morbidity rates can be made. But for several of the variables that have been examined in the previous chapter, an estimate can be made of the direction in which they would probably affect true morbidity rates if they could be measured precisely.

The Hutterite sect probably has the lowest frequency of psychoses among the four rural populations within the European and Judaeo-Christian complex of culture, but the experience of the population with this type of mental disorder is higher than that of the inhabitants of Formosa. This con-

Table 11—Qualitative Estimate of the Net Effect of Certain Correction Factors on the Comparative Ranking of Five Morbidity Surveys of Psychosis

CORRECTION FACTORS

Survey	Rank Order by Expectancy Ratio	Selective Migration of Psychotic Patients	Inadequacy of Field Work in Some Subarea or Subgroup	Under-enumeration of Nonhospital Cases	Under-enumeration of Recovered Cases	Estimated Corrected Rank Order
Arctic Norwegian Village	1 (Highest)	Downward	Insignificant	None	Insignificant	1
North Swedish Area	2	Downward	Unknown; probably slightly upward	Slightly upward	Upward	2
Ethnic Hutterites	3	None	Insignificant	None	Insignificant	4
West Swedish Island	4	Upward possibly 15-29%	Upward	Upward	Upward	3
Formosa Area	5 (Lowest)	Unknown	Probably insignificant	Probably insignificant	Upward	5

clusion, with all its tentativeness, can be a point of departure for a study of questions that cannot be answered by purely epidemiological methods. The latter can discover the presence or absence of quantitative differences, but the *why* and *how* of these quantitative findings remain to be explained. An intensive comparative study of the Hutterite, Chinese, and other populations would be required. Their genetic composition, physical health, psychological tendencies, social relationships, and cultural values would have to be analyzed in detail with the hope of identifying some patterned interrelationships that could account for the quantitative differences. In later chapters of this book the writers will provide some of the relevant information for the Hutterite culture.

Sex and Psychoses

Some psychoses are sex-correlated. For example, psychoses due to alcoholism are more common among males; manic-depressive reactions are more common among females. But if all psychoses are combined, there is no consistent *sex ratio* (the technical designation for the ratio of men to women).

Table 12—Sex Ratio of Psychotics and Total Population of Ten Morbidity Surveys

Survey	Total Number of Psychotics	Sex Ratio of Psychotics	Sex Ratio of Total Population
Ethnic Hutterites	53	.77	1.00
Arctic Norwegian Village	38	.73	1.05
Baltimore Eastern Health District	507	1.04	1.00
Bornholm Island	481	.61	.96
Thuringia Villages	200	.92	.96
Williamson County, Tennessee	156	1.33	1.04
West Swedish Island*	94	.75	1.04
North Swedish Area	107	1.38	1.14
Bavarian Villages, Rosenheim Area	21	2.45	1.00
Formosa Area	76	?	1.04

* No sex breakdown for the 94 cases living in 1944 was given. We estimated the sex ratio on the basis of a report for all enumerated mental cases, including both living and dead.

The Hutterite sex ratio of all psychotics was 0.77 men to

each woman patient. A high female morbidity was also found in the Arctic Norwegian Village, Bornholm Island, West Swedish Island, and Thuringia Villages studies. In the other four studies male patients predominated. The wide variation in the sex ratios of psychotics is puzzling. One can only speculate that they are related to chance, the predominance of certain sex-related types of psychoses, sex differentials in migration, or the differential readiness of the groups to apply the label "psychotic" to members of the two sexes.

In New York State more women than men were institutionalized each year until 1927. Since that time there has been a reversal in the sex ratio.[46] Males have been in excess. The Goldhamer-Marshall Expectancy Rates for psychoses in 1940 are consistently higher for males than for females in every age group. One possible explanation is that male psychotics are more frequently hospitalized in urbanized areas than female psychotics. This inference is made somewhat plausible by the Hutterite data, from a culture where there is no sex differential in treatment. Both men and women are cared for in their home. The lifetime morbidity rates of Hutterite women are more similar to conditional expectancy rates for New York State than is true of men. The Hutterite expectancy ratio, using New York State rates, is .5 for men and .8 for women. In 1940 New York State had fewer females than males in mental hospitals, in a proportion less than one would be led to expect on the basis of the Hutterite sex distribution of cases. In New York males might contribute a disproportionately large number to the population of mental hospitals.

Another, also nonbiological, explanation of this change in the sex ratio of patients has been suggested by J. L. Halliday. He notes that shifts in the sex ratio have been characteristic for a number of psychosomatic affections, and he speculates that these sex shifts may be an expression of changes in "personality type" as a result of social changes that led to female emancipation. "Thus certain of the psychosomatic affections which in the nineteenth century had preponderated in females (e.g., peptic ulcers, exophthalmic goiter and perhaps essential hypertension) during the twentieth century occurred increasingly in males; whereas others that had preponderated in males (e.g., diabetes) occurred increasingly in females."[47] Hutterite women are less emancipated than women in most American subgroups. The sex ratio of mental patients of this sect is similar to that of New York State in the nineteenth century.

Both of these explanations may contribute to an explanation of the sex ratio of Hutterite psychotic patients. But the phenomenon of sex shift in frequency rates clearly needs further study. This statistical fact may be a clue to an important finding about the role of social and cultural factors in the etiology of mental disorders.

New York State's High Record

Only one of the lifetime morbidity rates shown in Table 10 exceeds the Conditional Expectancy rates of hospitalized cases of psychoses in New York State. While these two measures of morbidity are only approximately comparable, the differences between the New York State Expectancy Ratio of 1.00 and the ratios of the ten populations are sufficiently large to warrant comment. The Hutterite group, which ranks third, has a ratio of only 0.62. The lifetime morbidity rates of psychotic disorders in the Hutterite population were not quite two-thirds of the approximately equivalent New York State measure in 1940. If we are to accept the Goldhamer-Marshall estimate that for every two hospitalized cases in New York there is probably one severe psychotic case not in an institution,[48] the expectancy ratio would be reduced to 0.42. The discrepancies between the New York State rates and those of most of the other studies are of even greater magnitude. The validity of actual size of these differences may be in doubt, but the fact that all but one of them are in the same direction is probably significant.

The question arises: Are these differences real or spurious? Can they be explained by differences of diagnostic standards and enumeration methods? Are they a reflection of the relative adequacy of New York State mental hospital facilities, availability of medical and social agencies skilled in diagnosing mental patients, and the difficulties of home care of patients? Do they reflect a drift to New York State of a good share of America's "lunatic fringe"? Are these high expectancy ratios a consequence of selective migration? All these explanations have an element of plausibility.

Ödegaard presents the view that high rates of psychoses result from "drift" or selective migration.[49] He inferred this conclusion from a study of Norwegian immigrants to the United States whose high frequency of psychotic breakdown was compared with the lower figure for Norwegians in Norway. In the previous chapter we have also shown that there is some evidence that migration factors were related to the frequency of psychoses in two of the Scandinavian studies reviewed. However, this migration theory is not supported by those who have made intensive studies of the distribution of mental disorder in American urban areas. Faris and Dunham question the drift hypothesis as an adequate explanation of the significant geographical differences they found in the incidence of psychosis in Chicago.[50] Hollingshead and Redlich report that the 857 schizophrenic patients located in their psychiatric census of New Haven were, as in Chicago, predominantly of lower class status, but there was no concentration of geographically transient and socially downward mobile persons among them. A study of residential moves showed that the New Haven schizophrenics did not "drift" into slums in significant numbers; most of them were born there. Only 1.3 per cent of the patients were rated in a lower social class than their parental family, whereas 4.4 per cent were in a higher class.[51]

In the light of this conflicting evidence, no conclusion can be drawn with confidence regarding the probable role of migration factors in explaining the high rates of psychosis in New York State. If "drift" could explain sociological differences in the frequency of psychotic breakdown, the etiological importance of genetic factors would be increased. The "drift" hypothesis can explain away as spurious or accidental significant social, economic, and cultural variations in the frequency of psychotic breakdown. But the contradictory findings of the New Haven study cannot be dismissed. They are a good reason for doubting that migration is a major variable in the etiology of the high rates of psychosis in New York State.

Age is almost certainly a major factor. In every population the chances of becoming mentally ill increase with age, but the rate of increase in New York State is unusually high in comparison with the data calculated for four of the ten populations. New York State's rates are generally above those of the four studies in every age group, but the discrepancy is greatest in the older years. The most plausible explanation of this high record has been well stated by Albert Deutsch:

The economic trend that has transformed our society from a dominantly agricultural to an overwhelmingly industrial one has carried in its wake a weakened respect and toleration for older people. . . . In the old days people took it for granted that mental enfeeblement often accompanies old age, as does physical enfeeblement. Nobody would have thought of sending an aged relative to an asylum just because he or she was confused or forgetful or garrulous. But in our small, crowded apartments, elderly folks get in the way of their children and grandchildren. They need special attentions that eat into a busy life. They arouse familial anxieties when they go out on the streets alone.[52]

The high morbidity findings of New York State also fit a

cultural theory. It is quite possible that the conflict pressures of modern life in an urban setting, in a population with a high proportion of immigrants who had to make drastic social and cultural adjustments, can lead to a cultural intensification of genetic, organic, and psychological predisposition for psychosis.

The Social Cohesion Factor

In all except the Hutterite population there were more schizophrenic than manic-depressive patients. The highest ratio of schizophrenic to manic-depressive reactions was 46.00 in the North Swedish Area. The remainder were all above 1.00 (See Table 9). The same ratio was only 0.23 in the Hutterite sect. Patients with a manic-depressive reaction constituted 73.6 per cent of all Hutterite persons diagnosed as psychotic. Among patients first admitted to a reporting United States mental hospital in 1928, 1938, and 1948, a much smaller and a decreasing proportion of cases were so diagnosed: 14.4, 11.1, and 6.0 per cent, respectively.

The differences are startling. One of the first explanations considered in the analysis was the possibility that the manic-depressive reaction category was the unconscious favorite of the psychiatric collaborator in the study. But this we doubt. The psychiatrist did not make his diagnostic judgments in a vacuum. All cases and their diagnosis were repeatedly discussed in conference with one or more members of the senior field work staff; they could hardly have missed so systematic a "bias." There certainly was no general disposition to avoid critical review of the judgment of a staff member even in matters related to his specialty. The Hutterite proclivity for depressive symptoms was not anticipated when the study was planned, nor did its extent become clearly apparent until most of the data had been collected. The full theoretical significance of this finding was not appreciated until much later. It cannot be a case of the investigators finding what they

looked for to prove a preconceived point. Depressive symptoms were common also among Hutterite psychoneurotic
patients. English and Hutterite teachers of 415 children of
school age, who were asked to rate independently the emotional adjustment of their pupils, checked "*Tendency Towards Depression*" as the most common negative symptom.*

The high Hutterite proportion of manic-depressive reactions could be in part a consequence of the thoroughness of
the enumeration of . cases. Manic-depressive patients often
recover. Such persons are easily missed in a census relying
largely on official sources. This view is supported by the
finding of Kurt H. Fremming,[53] who surveyed a largely
rural Danish Lutheran population with great intensity. He
found a large number of manic-depressive reaction cases who
had never been hospitalized and concluded that ". . . the
frequency of manic-depressive psychoses in the general population is 3-4 times higher than hitherto generally assumed."
It is undoubtedly true that hospital statistics of mental disorders underenumerate manic-depressive reactions. Society
rarely takes notice until a depressed patient becomes so
severely disoriented as to require hospitalization and/or threat-
ens to do violence to himself or others. Many persons committing suicide and murder suffered from manic-depressive
reactions which were not recognized in time to prevent these
tragic consequences. It is also difficult to make a differential
diagnosis between a severe neurotic depression and a mild
case of manic-depressive psychosis.

There would be enough uncontrolled variables in the various population studies to justify a possible dismissal of the
high Hutterite proportion of manic-depressive reaction cases
as being spurious, if it were not for the fact that the difference is very great. Depressive symptoms predominate not
only among Hutterite psychotic patients but also among less

---

* These findings will be discussed in detail in Chapter 7, dealing with
psychoneuroses.

disturbed persons and neurotics. In the Formosa Area, North Swedish Area, Arctic Norwegian Village, and West Swedish Island studies, where the research staff went far beyond a primary dependence on hospital and official sources in their screening of psychotic patients, the frequency or proportion of patients diagnosed as being manic-depressive is significantly smaller. The Hutterite percentage of cases is about three times as great as the comparable Formosa and West Swedish figures. In the Arctic Norwegian Village, where the screening process was particularly intensive and probably very few cases were missed, only 5 per cent of the patients were diagnosed as suffering from manic-depressive reactions. In our analysis we therefore conclude that the ratio of schizophrenic and manic-depressive reaction patients varies in different populations. If this assumption is correct, it would support the general theory that sociological factors play an important role in the way functional mental disorders are manifested in patients.

Tietze, Lemkau, and Cooper[54] have brought together evidence supporting this theory from a number of epidemiological surveys. They show that the proportion of manic-depressive psychosis patients is high, relatively to the number diagnosed as schizophrenic, among professional people, higher income groups, inmates of private mental hospitals, and residents of suburban areas. The reverse is true of persons with occupations of lower social status or lower income, inmates of public hospitals, and residents of the central areas of cities, where the population is more transient. Schizophrenia is the most common functional diagnosis among psychotic persons from these socially less integrated categories, and there is a significantly small proportion of cases of manic-depressive reaction. In general, many epidemiological findings of the frequency of functional psychoses show a high degree of internal consistency in support of the socio-cultural theory that manic depression is a disorder most common to persons who have a high degree of social cohesion and who are group centered. On the other hand, this diagnosis is much less common among persons who are social isolates and marginal. The latter category of persons is more likely to show symptoms of schizophrenia.

There also is further evidence in support of this social cohesion theory in the sex distribution of cases. In all human groups women have much higher rates of manic-depressive reaction than men. Although the role of women varies greatly in different families and different cultures, in most cases women are more cohesively identified with their family and group than are men within the same culture. The uniform statistical sex difference in rates of manic depression could well reflect this difference in social orientation. Women far more than men are identified with their family and group culture, and function as agents for its transmission to the next generation.

The Hutterites, who have the highest proportion of manic-depressive patients among the ten studies that have been compared, are also extreme in their emphasis on communal cohesiveness. There is much stress on religion, duty to God and society, and there is a tendency in their entire thinking to orient members to internalize their aggressive drives. Children and adults alike are taught to look for guilt within themselves rather than in others. The North Swedish Area, which has an unusually high proportion of schizophrenic cases and few manic-depressives, is populated by a much less socially cohesive population. Most inhabitants live in isolated farmsteads. There are many single males, particularly in the older age groups. While Dr. Böök leans to a genetic rather than a cultural explanation,* his findings certainly are consistent

---

* Dr. Böök has the following genetic explanation of his findings. It was furnished in a personal letter and is reproduced in toto:

It might interest you to know that the schizophrenics of this population display a very homogeneous clinical picture. There is

with the socio-cultural theory which relates schizophrenia to social disorganization, the absence of social cohesion, and a poorly integrated system of values.

Another brick in the supporting structure of this sociological theory is a clinical report by Frieda Fromm-Reichmann:

As a rule, people who suffer predominantly from manic-depressive mood swings seem to come from large families with multiple parental figures who share the responsibility for the guidance of the infant and child. There is no single significant adult who carries full responsibility for the child and to whom the child can relate himself meaningfully. Moreover, there is usually no one who is interested in the welfare of the child in its own right. The relatedness of the grown-ups to the child is determined by the purpose for which the child is needed and by the role into which it is cast according to the needs of the family. The needs of the families of these future manic-depressives are usually determined by the fact that these families belong to isolated minority groups to whom it seems very necessary to maintain given standards or the fight for survival. They accomplish these necessities by eagerly cultivating their part in a closely knit group unity.[55]

---

a total of 123 schizophrenics with a conclusive diagnosis who were discovered for the period of 1902-1949. About 85 per cent of these have been classified as catatonics. It is an atypical unsystematized type of catatonia mostly with periodic episodes of excitement, aggressiveness and very often a violence against other persons. My data support the view that this type of schizophrenia depends on a dominant major gene with a rather low penetrance (20 to 30 per cent). If the clinical features depend directly on a special gene which is prevalent in this population is hard to tell. There is always the possibility that these features, at least partly, are caused by the environment. It is also interesting to note that the majority of the catatonic cases displayed an athletic body type. Personally I think that what is today called schizophrenia includes a wide variety of psychotic reaction types, some of which may be almost exclusively environmental and others genetic. Very likely there are a number of different genes which under proper environmental conditions may produce schizophrenic reaction types. I believe that my study has shown that the genetic background of schizophrenia is not homogeneous. I thus don't agree with Dr. Kallmann's view that all types of schizophrenia belong to the same genetic entity and are inherited as simple recessives.

This "typical" case history comes close to describing the normative Hutterite socialization processes.

It does not fit the culture of Kenya Negroes who were studied by J. C. Carothers and that of most other tribal Negro Africans who were observed by white psychiatrists. Most of these reports agree that depressive symptoms, including severe guilt feelings and suicide tendencies, are extremely rare. Carothers explains these impressions with the hypothesis that ". . . the development of depression in standard forms is linked in high degree with personal integration, with a sense of personal continuity, and with a sense of responsibility for one's past and of a retribution that must follow one's sins."[56] He dismisses the alternative explanation that genuinely depressive subjects might not be recognized as mentally abnormal as being ". . . probably less true in Africa than in some parts of Europe where, by African standards, the 'normal' population seems depressed."*

These etiological clues are a step in the direction of explaining *why* social cohesion is correlated with the frequency of functional mental disorders. This is the crucial question if the goal is more knowledge about their causes, prevention, and treatment. The social cohesion theory also sets the stage for asking new questions, such as: How might social cohesion have an effect on the way people behave in a psychotic breakdown? One possible explanation can be found in the communication theory of Jurgen Ruesch and Gregory Bateson, who view psychopathology primarily as disturbances in the communication processes of perception, evaluation, and transmission of ideas within patients and between patients and

---

* It is, of course, also possible that the absence of these patients in hospitals is partly a consequence of life expectancy. Not many Africans live long enough to be exposed to the risk of manic-depressive reaction. Also, psychotic patients with depressive symptoms may be less likely to get into mental hospitals for Negro Africans. There are very few such institutions and Carothers points out that they can care for only a few of the most chronic and unmanageable patients.

their environment.[12] Certainly, the learning and socialization processes and the network of interpersonal and intrapersonal communication among people in socially cohesive groups differs significantly from that of persons who live with a relatively high degree of isolation from psychologically meaningful contact with others. In a cohesive group, the social structure pressures the individual to be a conformist. It creates trouble for those who have difficulty in accepting group norms. Guilt and withdrawal, which are so predominant in the symptomatology of depressed manic-depressive reaction cases, can be viewed as a logical by-product of these social structure factors. Conversely, in schizophrenia the severe disorientation to reality which is commonly found might be related to the fact that individuals in a fairly isolated social situation exist without clear guidance and social control.

The social cohesion theory which has been outlined is impressively plausible. The supporting data consists of ecological correlations, which provide significant points of departure for future research. However, the questions of *why* and *how* social cohesion factors are correlated with rates and proportions of different functional disorders cannot be studied epidemiologically. They will have to be tested in controlled studies of individuals; it is only there that the dynamic process of an emergent mental disorder can be observed with all its genetic, organic, psychological, social, and cultural complexities. However, if the social cohesion theory has validity it would provide a strong basis of support for social psychiatry. It would follow, for example, that appropriate changes in the social system, or in a mental hospital where patients live, can affect the way mental disorders are manifested.

Social cohesion is certainly not the only socio-cultural element worthy of study to understand the etiology of psychoses. That there must be other significant constellations of factors is illustrated by the fact that psychoses associated with drug addiction, alcoholism, and syphilis, which are common

in urban areas, were nearly absent in several of the rural populations. There were no cases among the socially cohesive
Hutterites but these disorders also were virtually absent in
three Scandinavian Lutheran populations who live in a much
less cohesive social system: the Bornholm Island, the West
Swedish Island, and the North Swedish Area. The rates were
about 0.2 per 1,000 persons aged 15 and over. In Thuringia
and in Bavaria the lifetime morbidity rate was larger, about
0.5 and 2.4 per 1,000 persons aged 15 and over. No case of
general paresis, the most common mental disorder related to
syphilis, was reported in both the Arctic Norwegian Village
and the Formosa studies.

We do not have good comparable census data from contrasting urban areas where a higher rate of these conditions
is usually found. It is a well established fact that the psychoses
associated with syphilis, alcoholism, and drugs account for a
good share of all Americans hospitalized for mental disorders.
In 1949, 16.5 per cent of all first admissions to United States
state hospitals for mental disorders were for conditions associated with alcoholism, syphilis, and drug addiction. In New
York State a little over 10 per cent of the first admissions for
psychoses suffered from such preventable mental diseases.[57]
Their rareness in several of the rural and religiously oriented
populations support the hypothesis that a variety of social
relation variables play a part in their prevention.

The Theory of Social-Genetic Drift

Our evidence in support of the socio-cultural factors is
strongest for manic-depressive reaction cases, but others have
found evidence that heredity is involved in the etiology of
this disorder.[58] Sixteen of the 39 Hutterite cases of manic-
depressive reaction were found to be fairly closely related to
at least one other patient suffering from this condition. While
none of the schizophrenic persons were related to one another,
two of them had a close relative with a manic-depressive reac-

tion. However, the number of schizophrenic cases in the Hutterite population is too small to justify a conclusion which could contradict the genetic theories of schizophrenia proposed by Franz J. Kallman[59] or Örnulv Ödegaard.*

In assessing the possible relationships of genetic factors for the low frequency of psychoses and the relatively high predominance of depressive symptoms among the Hutterites, it is important to point out that, historically speaking, the sect did not develop as a randomly selected human group. Individuals joined because they were converted to the Hutterite faith. Throughout the centuries of the long odyssey through Europe and to America, in the face of severe and chronic persecution, only the most faithful and group-conscious were able to survive, and to remain members of the sect. Considering these circumstances, the Hutterite way of life had little to attract what some genetically oriented psychiatrists call "schizothymic" personality types.† The communal organiza-

---

* Örnulv Ödegaard, "Emigration and Mental Health," *Mental Health,* Vol. XX (1936), 546-553. Ödegaard notes that schizophrenia is very prevalent among Norwegians in Minnesota who may have had to deal with unusual social stresses in connection with their migration from their homeland. He found, however, upon examination of their individual case histories, that the immigrant status of patients seemed to have been unimportant in their clinical picture. Largely on this basis he rejects the environmental theory and postulates as more plausible the explanation that immigrants are a self-elected group, with a higher-than-average representation of schizo-thymic persons and a lower-than-average representation of syntonic types. However, the rareness of data on the migrant status of Norwegian immigrant patients in U.S. hospitals could be a reflection of the psychocentric bias of most psychiatrists, clinical psychologists, and psychiatric social workers. Their clinical training predisposes them to see psychic problems largely in intrapersonal terms. They are less likely to ask sociological and value orientation questions. Such information, when it is volunteered, may not be dictated in the brief case records because it is deemed irrelevant to the resolution of the Oedipus complex or other such psychodynamic assumptions.

† Those who use this typology of what they assume to be generically transmitted basic personality types describe their characteristics as follows: SCHIZOTHYMIC: Persons who tend to be sensitive, seclusive, and sometimes suspicious and queer, and eccentric; they have only few and loose ties with their fellows and with the community.

tion of the sect was more attuned to meeting the needs of "cyclothymic" persons, the personality type most common among manic-depressive reaction patients. If there is any degree of validity to this psychogenetic typology, (and this has not been established) it would not be surprising to find modern Hutterites to be a group including many "cyclothymic" personalities. Certainly the history of the Hutterite sect supports a presumption that throughout the four centuries of its existence, genetic and social factors have reinforced each other to produce a highly unusual distribution of functional psychoses.

The Validity of Socio-Cultural Causation

In a study of the causal functions of social system factors, their patterned, or *Gestalt,* aspects must be kept in mind. Human life can exist under a great diversity of conditions. One mechanism which facilitates this social-anthropological variety is the tendency in nature towards the development of equilibrium or compensatory mechanisms. For example, in a group where the opportunities for women are limited to a few roles, such as being a mother and housewife, there is often little cultural expectation for women to distinguish themselves in any other way. Among the Hutterites the potential stress of such limitations on women to express their personality may be balanced somewhat by the fact that they are given considerable recognition for the cheerful acceptance of socially approved female roles. In general, in the social and cultural aspects of human existence, as in its genetic, organic, and psychological attributes, one finds that positive and negative traits offset each other to produce a balanced pattern that permits people to function and survive. It also follows that a specific cultural trait need not have the same positive

---

CYCLOTHYMIC: Persons who tend to be communicative, practical, sociable, occasionally moody but generally well integrated, mature personalities.[60]

or negative mental health implication for all human groups. Among the rural Hutterites, an independent personality who likes to do things "on his own" and to differentiate himself from others, experiences much social disapproval. In the rural atmosphere of Massachusetts in 1840, or in the rural Arctic Village studied by Bremer in 1940, such an individualist might have had considerable social status and approval. Any analysis of the causal functions of culture and social relationships must proceed from a recognition of the complexity of what men do can be understood only by relating human acts or attributes to the total way of life within which they are found. It is affected by every dimension of existence, including genetic, organic, psychological, social, and other cultural attributes.

The procedure to lump in one category a great variety of different psychotic conditions makes the most of our cross-cultural comparisons of the frequency of psychoses. It was decided upon because it provided a fairly stable and objectively measurable index which was somewhat independent of the great variations in diagnostic terminology of different psychiatrists. This advantage was offset by the fact that any given frequency of psychoses can reflect many different positive, neutral, and negative mental health patterns. For example, the Hutterite and North Swedish Area populations differed only moderately in their frequency of psychoses. In the former, however, most of the patients had manic-depressive reactions, whereas in the latter, schizophrenia was the most common form of psychosis.

One of the logical consequences of comparing combined frequencies with each other is the probability that only very pronounced, stable, and consistent cultural or social patterns can have enough effect on personal behavior to be measurable by so crude an index as the overall frequency of psychoses. On this basis the question of the validity of the measured differences in the expectancy ratios of psychoses needs to be

considered. Is the true lifetime morbidity expectation of Hutterites significantly different from that of persons living in
New York State, in an Arctic Norwegian village, or on Formosa? And if some of these differences are significant, how
much confidence can be placed in an interpretation that sociological factors are involved?

There can be no doubt that cultural factors can encourage
or inhibit the conditions that lead to certain organic psychoses.
Within our own lifetime we have experienced the virtual disappearance in the United States of chronic brain syndromes
associated with avitaminosis, especially pellagra. There is also
evidence in our comparative study that the frequency of
mental disorders associated with syphilis, alcoholism, and
drugs is low or absent in certain human groups. This is probably no accident. The social and cultural milieu of these rural
people functions to reduce their exposure to sexual relationships with members of out-groups. Some of them also impose
strict taboos on the use of alcohol and drugs.

However, the case in support of the theory that sociological factors are also significant for other functional or psychogenetic psychoses is more complicated. Two of the best
contemporary epidemiological studies failed to reveal a significant difference in the rate of all psychoses in groups which
differed considerably in cultural and socio-economic status.
Goldhamer and Marshall[61] found no long-term increase during the century from about 1840 to 1940 in the incidence of
hospitalized cases of functional psychoses of early and middle life. Bremer[62] divided the population of his arctic village
into two approximately equal groups on the basis of their
socio-economic status. There was no significant difference
in the lifetime morbidity rate of psychoses between 636 residents who were economically secure and had relatively high
status in the community, and 689 villagers who were economically insecure and were engaged in occupations of
lower social rank.

These findings, reinforced by our observation that functional psychoses occur in as protected and secure a social system as the Hutterite, might indicate that genetic and constitutional factors should be regarded as the primary etiological suspect. Cultural factors could be viewed as being of a low order of relevance for the incidence of psychoses in a population. However, other explanations of these data are possible and plausible. The psychological traumas of life in Massachusetts in 1940 may be no greater in their net impact on personality than were the stresses of a more rural society undergoing the growing pains of an industrial revolution a century earlier. The socio-economic status differences in Bremer's Arctic Village were not very great, and may not have been of sufficient magnitude to have a measurable effect on the tendency of individuals to react to life stresses with psychotic manifestations.

The finding of this study that there are large cross-cultural differences in the expectancy ratios of psychoses, and the evidence that populations varied significantly in their apparent susceptibility to schizophrenia and manic-depressive reactions, add great weight to the hypothesis that major cultural differences have an effect on the frequency of psychoses in a population. However, it is probable that only pronounced, stable, and well integrated cultural traits can have the function of moderately increasing or decreasing the frequency of functional psychotic reactions. Genetic, organic, and psychological factors will always be sufficient to produce a minimum of functional psychotic breakdown. This theory is in harmony with the observation that the overall frequency of psychoses was highest in the Arctic Norwegian Village which Bremer describes as an extremely stressful social setting. Among the Hutterites the rate was much lower. Many of the social stresses of the American and European scene are reduced or absent in this socially cohesive system.

This partly society- and culture-dynamic theory is all the

more plausible in view of the considerable body of data indicating that personal stresses in America's urban scene are frequently associated with economic insecurity and the breakdown of close interpersonal, family, and community ties. Goldhamer and Marshall found that despite the absence of a long-term increase in the incidence of hospitalized cases of functional psychoses over a period of a century, there were short-term changes which coincided with major social catastrophes such as wars and depressions.[61] Sociological variables therefore would appear to be significant in the etiology of functional psychoses, but there are definite limits to the degree to which the absolute frequency of psychoses can be modified by social system factors.* For example, the extreme cohesiveness of the Hutterites, which may contribute to their low frequency of schizophrenia, may be significant for the relatively high proportion of manic-depressive reactions among psychotic members of the sect.

If this theory is correct, it would follow that minor social and cultural patterns, particularly if they are not well integrated throughout the social system, and if they are not extreme, will not have a readily measurable impact on the frequency of psychoses. For example, fluctuations of fashions of disciplinary practice from emphasis on permissiveness to stress on compliance with adult norms, which have been supported by American pediatric experts from time to time, are probably unimportant for adult mental health. However, in families where permissiveness is extreme or is a symptom of parental rejection, and where this rejecting attitude is reinforced by many other child-rearing practices from infancy throughout the entire period of socialization, an experience

---

* The writers were unable to interpret the Formosa findings since the published report did not include enough psychological, social, and cultural data for such a purpose. However, if this theory is correct, an intensive clinical study of the social life and culture of Formosa should reveal that it is even more conducive to social adjustment than the Hutterite way of life.

of such consistency may well be significant. The impact of social relations and cultural values on psychoses is not so great or so direct that fairly isolated norms or experiences will show up as quantitatively measurable.

This theory has an optimistic implication. It follows that a great deal of consistency and traumatic impact is necessary to increase the number of functional psychoses in a human group. No child can be "ruined" by occasional parental or group thoughtlessness. But there is also a more sobering caution. Large-scale preventive hygiene programs are not likely to show quick and dramatic effects that can be demonstrated statistically. And they are not likely to be effective at all unless they are well integrated and supported throughout the entire social system. Preventive mental hygiene would not appear to be a job for piecemeal social action. The home, the school, the place of work, and other social institutions need to work on an integrated long-range program if it is to have a measurable effect. There are no "quickie" techniques in the battle against functional psychoses.

Some degree of psychotic breakdown cannot be avoided in any human group, irrespective of cultural and social milieu, but the traumatic impact of such breakdown for the patient, the family, and his community may be more culturally relative. In any case, the qualitative impact is a problem that can be considered separately from the quantitatively measurable effects. Sociological factors are probably most significant in their clinical effect on the way in which psychotic breakdown takes place. This qualitative theory is supported by the finding that social cohesion lends itself to an explanation of many of the differences found between cultural groups and sex categories in their relative susceptibility to schizophrenia and manic-depressive reactions. Additional documentation will be provided in later chapters of this book. Social system factors will be related to the more qualitative aspects of mental disorders, their severity, and their treatment.

6.

Psychoses

IN PREVIOUS chapters the relations of cultural variables to psychoses were studied by epidemiological and comparative methods. In this and in following chapters, a more clinical analysis will be made of mental disorder cases and symptoms found in the Hutterite population. The emphasis will be on locating more specific cultural traits and social relationships that may be significantly related to specific symptoms of disorder and their treatment.

It may be recalled from Chapter 3 that 53 Hutterites were diagnosed by the study staff as having been psychotic at some time. The *lifetime morbidity rate* was 6.2 patients per 1,000 or 12.6 per 1,000 persons 15 years of age or more. Fourteen of these individuals were actively ill during the summer of 1951. An additional six patients were ill but showed improvement. The combined *active case morbidity* was 4.7 per 1,000 persons aged 15 or over. At least 29 persons were diagnosed as having recovered from a psychosis. In four other cases there was insufficient information about the recovery status. Of the twenty who were ill during the summer of 1951, none were institutionalized. Eleven of them were sufficiently ill to justify their commitment to a mental hospital if their families should request it—an estimated rate of hospitalizable cases of 1.3 per 1,000 Hutterites or 2.6 per 1,000 aged 15 or over.

The frequency of psychoses is correlated with age in all populations. Horatio M. Pollock[63] points out that schizophrenia and manic-depressive psychoses generally develop in the third, fourth, and fifth decades of life. General paresis, alcoholic, and involutional psychoses come in the fourth, fifth, and sixth decades. Senile and arteriosclerotic psychoses show up in old age, in the sixth, seventh, and eighth decades. The distribution of psychoses in the Hutterite population showed the same general age trends. Estimates of onset of illness were made by our staff within broad age ranges, although the information on this point furnished by the Hutterite informants often was vague, particularly for persons whose illness began long ago. Usually there was no dramatic event to mark clearly the onset of the disease. None of the cases became psychotic before the age of 17. All of the schizophrenics showed signs of illness before they turned thirty. Most manic-depressive psychoses had their onset during the third, fourth, and fifth decades of life. Three persons who became ill after the age of 75 were diagnosed as having senile psychoses.

There also was nothing unusual in the Hutterite sex distribution of psychotic cases. As in most other studies, manic-depressive reactions were found to be much more common among the women than the men.[64] The ratio was nearly 8 to 5. The consistency of the age and sex distribution of Hutterite psychotics with what we know about these factors from other studies gives some confidence to the supposition that the diagnostic judgments of our staff are broadly within the range of contemporary general psychiatric practice.

Manic-Depressive Reactions

Depression was the most common reaction to stress in the sect. In 39 of the 53 cases, depression of mood with mental and motor retardation, perplexity, or agitation was prominent in the symptomatology. Most of the cases, 33 in number, were diagnosed as manic-depressive reactions of the depressed type. In one case there was enough excited behavior, flight of ideas, and elated effect to make the diagnosis of manic type. Five cases were recorded as mixed manic because of their restlessness, agitation, flight of ideas, extreme talkativeness, and occasional threat of violence.

There were 4.6 persons per 1,000 Hutterites or 9.3 per 1,000 aged 15 and over who were diagnosed as manic-depressive. Included in this category were cases of involutional melancholia. Twenty of the patients became ill between the ages of 40 and 59. Only three of the cases were acutely ill during the summer of 1951; five others were ill but showed signs of improvement. They seemed to have passed the peak of their emotional disturbance. Twenty-seven patients were definitely known to have recovered.

The psychiatrist would have been ready to recommend commitment to a mental hospital for only one of the acutely ill patients. In about thirteen of the other improved or recovered cases a commitment could have been recommended when the patients were more seriously ill.

Prospects for recovery of Hutterites with a manic-depressive reaction were good. Their recovery ratio of about 69 per cent was in accord with general American hospital experience, for, according to Coleman, ". . . seventy per cent of hospitalized cases recover within one year of first admission."[65] In our study, where adequate social function rather than hospital discharge was the criterion, recovery was somewhat slower. About a third of the patients recovered within a year, a third within one to five years, and four persons after

longer periods. For the remaining cases data were inadequate
to estimate length of illness. In general the prognosis for depressed patients in the Hutterite culture was better than that
found by Lloyd H. Ziegler and Philip H. Heersema[66] in a
follow-up study in 1940-41 of 84 *nonhospitalized* depressed
patients who were seen at the Mayo Clinic during 1926-27.
The chances for improvement or recovery (about 42 per
cent) were lower for the Mayo Clinic group than for the
Hutterites. The Mayo group also had more subsequent hospitalization (six cases) and suicide (seven cases).

We did not hear of, or see, any Hutterite patient whose
depression alternated with a manic phase.* Very few expressed verbal threats of aggression. There was no instance
of injury to others during a state of manic excitement, but
five patients reported suicidal impulses which can be viewed
as instances of internalized aggression. Two suicides actually
did occur.†

Hutterites refer to a depression as *Anfechtung*, by which is
meant "temptation by the devil." The course of symptomatology is not unusual, but the content of the delusions and
the verbal production of the Hutterite depressives seem to
be greatly colored by their notion that the disorder is a
spiritual or religious trial by God. Several patients mentioned

---

* The "forced marriage" of manic and depressive symptoms dates
back to Kraepelin's classification system at the turn of the twentieth century. The psychiatric usage of the term "manic-depressive reaction" is
dynamically misleading; it may also be psychologically damaging. It
implies that all persons with depressive moods are likely to exhibit manic
behavior and tend to have recurrent spells of illness. Thomas A. C.
Rennie[67] in a relevant study found that only about 25 per cent of his
208 manic-depressive cases were cyclocyclic. There is much evidence that
many psychotic patients with a predominantly depressive symptomatology
are very different in etiology and prognosis from those who show cycles with
manic and depressive phases. They should be enumerated in a separate
category.

† We excluded these persons from the 1951 lifetime morbidity case
count. One of them left his colony as a young man and killed himself
several years later in a fit of despondency. They are the only Hutterites
known to have committed suicide since the arrival of the sect in the 1870's.

the Book of Job, in which God tests the sincerity and the strength of a man's belief and trust in Him. Hutterites believe that depression is a condition which befalls "good" people. Little guilt or shame is attached to such an experience. Most ex-patients readily discussed it. Several informants mentioned that their depression started suddenly. They were able to recall the exact time, such as being at church on a certain day, at which they suddenly felt that something had overcome them.

Manic-depressive persons, both before and after their illness, were generally well integrated in the community. They included a somewhat larger proportion of leaders and their wives than would be expected to occur on a random basis. During their illness they were often relieved of responsibility and put on more routine jobs. They were generally restored to their position of active responsibility after recovery. During most of their depressed period, almost two-thirds were able to do some of the regular work expected of them. Few were ever so ill that they could not look after their children or eat with other adults in the dining room, or that they required constant watching to keep them from doing physical harm to themselves or others. In about another 25 per cent of the 39 cases the depression was immediately preceded by a symptom of severe physical illness, such as cancer, dropsy, epilepsy, pneumonia, or piles, or by the death of a close friend or relative. In five of the 24 women the depression occurred after childbirth.

Depressive patients were usually taken to a doctor, but few received any psychiatric attention. None were in a mental hospital. Two were given electro-convulsive therapy. A few patients were watched carefully if there was any evidence of suicidal tendencies. Hutterites consider suicide to be one of the most serious of all possible sins; the finality of the act precludes any absolution through confession, repentance, or communal punishment. The person who takes his own life is thought to be condemned to eternal hell. Relatives and friends are particularly anxious to prevent such a tragedy.

The dynamic picture will be illustrated by two case summaries. It should be noted that neither of them describes any living or deceased person. They show only clinical pictures abstracted from a number of cases. Names and other identifying information are fictitious.

1. Leader, Male, Age 59   Diagnosis:
                                 Manic-Depressive Reaction
                                 Depressed Type

The patient has recovered from a brief depressive attack which he had at the age of 20, before he was married. He was the eldest of 12 children. He had long crying spells, felt worthless, and had suicidal thoughts. The illness was confirmed by himself and several other informants who knew him as a boy. He is now an ex-farm-manager of his colony and is greatly respected. He is rigidly orthodox in his religious views and has been ever since his youth. His stepsister also had a depressive attack. He described his experience as follows:

> It came on very suddenly like a shock. When I was sitting down sometimes it just raised me up and whenever I saw a knife or a rope the devil said to me use it and end your troubles, there is no other way out. You are lost anyway. But I hurried away from such places and wept bitterly with streams of tears running out of my eyes and prayed to God. I would not believe that He would like me to do this but believe me the prayers have got to be in earnest with tears out of your eyes and not only once but over and over, and don't set a time to God but be patient and wait until God thinks it's time. Do your duty and keep on praying for help till he comes and helps. I am now well and thank the Lord that saved me.

2. Young Married Woman,   Diagnosis:
     Age 29   Manic-Depressive Reaction
                                 Depressed Type
                                 (A borderline case, classified as psychotic rather than psychoneurotic.)

The patient, an attractive young married woman was seen by the psychiatrist and several other staff members. She explained that after her first pregnancy she had felt rather moody for a short period. A year later, during the early part of her second pregnancy, she left her home colony to live with her older sister, who offered to take care of her because she had broken her leg. She felt very close to this sister, who had helped to rear her after their mother had died of pneumonia. The sister was a somewhat domineering but sympathetic person. She had very high status among both men and women in her own and in neighboring colonies. She was widely consulted because of her wisdom in matters of health, child rearing, and family problems. In her lifetime she had had a more severe attack of depression, but she was completely recovered at the time of our study.

The patient felt strongly identified with her and frequently compared what she regarded as her own modest accomplishments in life with those of her competent and motherly sister. While she was being taken care of in the latter's home, the patient found it more and more difficult to sleep. Often she was unable to complete her thoughts. Once she had a dream that her sister gave her a sharp sword. She also had fantasies that her child would be born a defective because "how can a person like myself have a normal child?" She felt guilty about undefined "evil" thoughts and went to the preacher to confess these "sins," with a request for church punishment. He explained to her that she had done nothing for which she could be punished. This response from the minister made her feel worse rather than better. She continued to feel obsessively dissatisfied with herself and often got up early in the morning to pray. She ruminated a great deal about her "worthlessness."

Before her confinement she returned to her husband's colony. There she was delivered of a healthy baby, but her emotional outlook did not change. She recalled that about that time she had impulses to jump into water and do something to her baby. She felt the devil was responsible for these "temptations." She intensified her prayer during such periods. She took care of her infant, but said she had no "joy in it." Her husband had to do much of her work in the home.

The patient knew that she was ill. The colony sent her to a Winnipeg psychiatrist to take electric shock treatments, but stopped them when they did not seem to help her. Later she wrote the following letter to another doctor:

Dear Doctor:

I made up my mind to write you a few words and to let you know that I am not well yet. My husband is awfully good to me. I really must get well to be more of a helper to him. Our colony will branch out in the spring and the men elected him manager. He should not have to spend so much time at home to help me with just the two children the Lord gave me.

I have still got a terrible strain in the left side of my face and specially in temples, my tongue is still numb. I got no joy in nothing. I do a little sewing which I do correct too but for instance I can do no housework. If I make up my mind this minute to do something the next it's gone.

And I was the kind of woman that never could be without work before I got this depression. I know that I was that way before and when I try to do so again it seems there is something that presses me to the ground.

I had no baby for over a year and a half. All doctors advise me not to get pregnant before I am over my depression. I would like to know how you feel about it. My sister and I think probably it would make a change. I was in good health while carrying my first baby.

I can sleep quite well but I get up with such drowsy feelings. I take care of my children but I got no joy in them. I often tell my husband I take care of them while I am with them but if they should become sick and die I wouldn't feel sorry either. So please be so kind and take interest in my letter and let me know what would be best to do for me. Maybe God has given you wisdom that you know more by now about Mental Depression that through his power you could do something for me to bring me back to normal health.

With lots of hope for the future.

Thanks in advance,

(Signature)

In these and other manic-depressive reaction cases, the loss of self-esteem and obsessive ruminations over sins and omissions were perhaps the most common symptoms. The culture of a Hutterite village is conducive to the development of such sentiments. From early infancy most parents and all colony school teachers are engaged in a conscious effort to "break the child's will" so that he can grow up into a "good" person. Among the qualities that are particularly highly valued are a strong conscience, the submission of impulsive wants to community expectations, and the repression of rebellious attitudes against the authority of the mores and of individuals in positions of power, who are identified with these basic value assumptions of the group. The impact of social and cultural factors can be seen in all the case histories, although it must be noted that the great majority of Hutterites, who grow up in the same traditionalistic atmosphere, never show symptoms of a manic-depressive reaction. The conclusion that social and cultural variables may be a necessary condition for this psychosis does not carry an implication that these factors are sufficient for its etiology. Psychological and perhaps genetic factors are involved in the selective process whereby only a few of the many Hutterites respond to their fairly uniform cultural milieu with manic-depressive reaction symptoms.

Schizophrenia

Schizophrenia is the most common diagnosis of cases in American mental hospitals, but as Otto Fenichel points out, "The diversity of schizophrenic phenomenon makes a comprehensive orientation more difficult than in any other class of mental disorders. Occasionally it has been doubted whether a comprehensive orientation is possible at all and whether the diverse schizophrenic phenomena actually have anything in common."[68] If this theory is correct, and if schizophrenia is not a nosological entity but embraces a whole group of diseases, researchers are not likely to find it very useful. Generalizations about etiology cannot be made about a number of disorders that do not belong to the same order of phenomena but are lumped together only because it has not been possible to devise a more meaningful system of classification. This theory about the nature of schizophrenia is not shared by all psychiatrists, particularly those who, like Franz J. Kallman, are engaged in research which presumes that schizophrenia is a specific nosological entity transmitted genetically.

In the application of this diagnostic term to Hutterite patients, we were guided by the American Psychiatric Association Diagnostic and Statistical Manual definition which equates schizophrenic reaction with the Kraepelinian term *dementia praecox,* formerly in wide use:

It represents a group of psychotic reactions characterized by fundamental disturbances in reality relationships and concept formation, with affective, behavioral, and intellectual disturbances in varying degrees and mixtures. The disorders are marked by strong tendency to retreat from reality, by emotional disharmony, unpredictable disturbances in stream of thought, regressive behavior, and in some, by a tendency to deterioration of personal habits and moral controls.[69]

The symptoms usually develop slowly and have no regular sequence of growth. Most frequently they have their onset during late adolescence or the earlier years of adulthood. The diagnosis is applied only to patients whose pattern of disturbances appears to have no organic basis.

There were nine cases of schizophrenia among the ethnic Hutterites living in the summer of 1951.* Four individuals were diagnosed as cases of chronic and undifferentiated schizophrenia, four as catatonic, and one as paranoid. The lifetime morbidity rate was 1.1 person per 1,000 or 2.1 per 1,000 persons aged 15 and over. These patients constituted 17 per cent of all diagnosed psychotics. This proportion of schizo-

---

* Included was one paranoid schizophrenic who became sick after having left the colony. Excluded were two cases of catatonic schizophrenia and one unclassified case, a mother and two sons. They were brought into a colony by the husband, a convert to the Hutterite faith. This family was not of Hutterite ethnic origin and had not experienced the Hutterite socialization process.

phrenics was close to the one in five ratio of such patients first admitted to United States state mental hospitals in 1928, 1938, and 1948,[70] but the Hutterite ratio of schizophrenic to all psychotic patients was the lowest of the ten population surveys. All but one of the Hutterite schizophrenics were chronically ill. One case was showing improvement. Another person, who left his community and is now gainfully employed, may have made a social recovery.

Schizophrenic patients were well known throughout the Hutterite sect. Their names and some of their symptoms were mentioned repeatedly by many informants in geographically widely dispersed communities. The manifestations of illness were usually puzzling and sometimes disturbing to many people. Only the one possibly recovered case was never contacted by our staff. He was diagnosed in a midwestern state mental hospital, where he was confined for six months. Five of the nine patients were taken by Hutterites to see a psychiatrist. Our staff psychiatrist estimated that seven of the eight active schizophrenic patients could be recommended for legal commitment to a mental hospital if their families wanted it. All but one of the patients were living at home with their immediate families. The exception was a middle-aged bachelor who suffered from hallucinations and showed mildly regressive behavior. The colony built a separate cottage for him. His sister brought him food and clothing, as the patient was usually unwilling to eat in the community dining room. The patient was at liberty to roam around the grounds of the hamlet. He had a key to his cottage, which he kept locked whenever he left it.

Schizophrenia tends to strike Hutterites early in life. In four cases the disorder was first recognized between the ages of 17 and 24; in the five others the illness became apparent before the patients had reached their thirtieth birthday. Four of the nine patients were married. In 1951 they had an average of seven children. The women continued to have children after their illness became clearly recognized. All of them participated in some of the household chores, although they could not be given much responsibility. They normally ate with the other adults in the dining room. They often attended the daily church service, although some patients were sufficiently regressed to resist these forms of social participation. Withdrawal was the most common pathological symptom. Hallucinations, delusions, and mildly paranoid features also occurred, but none of the patients were dangerous. There was no dynamic uniformity in these nine cases except that the emotional difficulties seemed to center on intimate personal relationships rather than social or cultural interactions.

Hutterites were less likely to explain schizophrenia in religious terms as they did manic-depressive reactions. Supernatural forces or the devil were not thought to be involved. Several cases were explained as "broken nerves," fright, grief over a death, and disappointment in love. Others were thought to have taken "too much medicine" or "jumped into water when young." In one case it was explained that "a doctor poked around in the nose and hit the brain." If there was anything unusual about schizophrenic cases in this culture, it was their ability to function socially at a moderate level of adequacy. Extreme antisocial acts, severe regression, or excitement, so common in the schizophrenic patients in mental hospitals, were not observed. One factor may be the excellent and generally thoughtful custodial care given by people who have some affectionate regard for the patient.

A typical clinical picture is shown in the following composite case history. Its content is not descriptive of any actual living or deceased Hutterite:

Young, Charles, Age 35   Diagnosis:
                                             Schizophrenia
                                             Catatonic Type
    Young Charlie lives in a colony in South Dakota. His family thinks he is recovering nicely from a "bad sickness of the mind."

He is beginning to mix socially with people. He does some work in the chicken barn, where his uncle is the manager. Relatives and neighbors praise him for the work done, even though it often takes much urging. His uncle rarely goes to town on colony business without asking him to come along. "It seems to cheer him up, although sometimes he won't even answer a question on whether he wants to come along." Charlie has some insight into his illness and occasionally speaks freely about some of the things which worry him.

Charlie's father died suddenly shortly after deserting his wife in 1916. She was two months pregnant at the time. Mrs. P. experienced a deep emotional shock, which she thinks caused harm to the fetus. She had been one of the most popular girls of her set and her very bright and hard-working husband was looked upon as a potential leader. As colony carpenter, he had much contact with outsiders, such as lumber dealers and hardware salesmen. Apparently they influenced him to leave the colony and try life on his own.

Charlie's delivery was without complications. His mother nursed him for about a year and does not recall having had any special problems except that he had an attack of chicken pox before he was old enough to sit up. He also had several convulsive attacks in his third year, during what may have been a febrile illness. His development was quite within the normal range of experiences for a Hutterite child. He was toilet trained during his first year of life, talked quite well at two, and went to the kindergarten at three where he mixed readily with other children. At the age of six he entered grade school and finished the eighth grade as an average student at the age of 15.

During his last two years of school he suffered from occasional headaches, sometimes accompanied by spells of vomiting. When he was approximately eighteen, he showed a progressive lack of interest in his work. His movements slowed, he had to be urged to get out of bed in the morning, and he spent more and more time by himself, brooding and staring into space. He responded gruffly to inquiries about what was troubling him and asked to be left alone. These periods alternated with periods when he seemed to regain his "old self," during which he had normal relationships with people.

At the age of 23 he was drafted. He shared Hutterite pacifist convictions and was assigned to a camp of conscientious objectors.

There he became progressively more moody and uncommunicative. He was finally discharged. After his return to the colony, his condition became worse. He began talking to himself and would sit alone for many hours in his room, staring into space. He became angry with those who tried to engage him in conversation or encourage him to help them in their work. Sometimes he ran off into the bushes, where he stayed for several hours. He often worried about masturbation. There were some days when he seemed to be all right and even showed romantic interest in a girl.

The colony took him to several local general practitioners. They prescribed sedatives. His mother and sisters also gave him a variety of patent medicines, but none of them seemed to help. His uncle then took him to a Chicago medical center for observation. There he was diagnosed as schizophrenic. The colony was advised to send him to a mental hospital. This was done. He stayed there six months and received both electric and insulin shock treatments. He was visited frequently by members of his immediate family and the colony. When his condition did not improve, he was taken home.

After his return from the hospital he spoke more about his father than ever before. He had fantasies about visiting his father to urge him to return to the Hutterite way of life. At other times he spoke very aggressively of his father and wanted to punish him. Sometimes he would express great pity for his mother: "You must have had a hard life," he once said. At other times he threatened to hit her, and on a few occasions he did so. Several times he ran away from the colony. Usually two or three men were needed to bring him home by force.

Charlie knows he is ill, complains of an inability to concentrate, but was very responsive in the interview with our staff psychiatrist. He does not blame anyone for his illness and said spontaneously that he would not marry until he is fully recovered.

As regards treatment, Young Charlie is surrounded by people with considerable therapeutic insight. His sisters sleep in the same room because he fears to be alone. His uncle spends much time with him and tries to interest him in others. There is a shortage of men of working age in this particular colony. Young Charlie knows that his work really *is* important. He is urged, but never pushed, to work. He is praised for what he does. He is rarely contradicted, reprimanded, or punished. Every effort is made to protect him from conflict or challenge with which he cannot cope. Everybody in the community, including children, know that Charlie's condition is an illness. He is the object of sympathy rather than ridicule. People feel that he is an integral part of the community, and Young Charlie reciprocates this identification.

The eight other Hutterite patients diagnosed as schizophrenic showed a variety of regressive trends to lower psychosexual levels of personality function. The writers were unable to find some common dynamic tendencies, except that whatever the nature of the psychopathology, *symptoms were rarely extreme* in their severity or their antisocial tendencies. This fact may mean that sociological factors have only a limited effect on the manifestation of schizophrenia. An even more plausible explanation is that a generalizable typology cannot be expected among schizophrenic patients; this diagnosis is probably a catchall for a variety of disorders, which have so far defied all attempts at a more meaningful classification.

Acute and Chronic Brain Disorders

Manic-depressive reactions and schizophrenia accounted for 48 of the 53 psychotics diagnosed in the Hutterite epidemiological survey. The remaining five cases were disorders with a predominantly organic etiology. There were three senile psychotics, two men and one woman, who showed conditions typically associated with this diagnosis; forgetfulness, childishness, and inability to look after their physical needs without help. They represented 4 per cent of the living Hutterites on December 30, 1950, who were 70 years old or more. Their average age at the time their illness was first noticed was 73; in 1951 their average age was 79. The staff psychiatrist would have been willing to recommend the commitment of two of the three patients to a mental hospital on request of their families. But in fact all of them received excellent custodial care in their homes, and none had ever been a public charge.

There was one case of toxic psychosis in which the patient had hallucinations during an attack of pneumonia with a temperature of over 104 degrees. It is interesting that during his toxic condition depressive features predominated. The patient stated upon recovery that he was battling with himself because he felt guilty for not being religious enough. He also had wild nightmares about "impossible things that could not be told in either English or German." Finally, there were two cases of postencephalitic Parkinsonism, but only one of these was psychotic. He could be committed to a mental hospital. The other had predominantly neurological signs and within the limits of his illness he participated well in work and community life.

The proportion of organic mental disorders in the Hutterite population is exceedingly small, 9 per cent. In contrast, approximately half of the patients admitted for the first time to state hospitals for mental disease in 1948 or 1949 were definitely diagnosed as suffering from mental disorders due to organic conditions.[71] This low proportion of organic psychotic conditions in part may be related to the extremely youthful character of the population; many organic psychoses are conditions of middle and old age. The fact that Hutterites are protected by their way of life from exposure to drugs, unlimited amounts of alcohol, and syphilis is another factor in the relative rareness of organic psychoses. The high prestige older people enjoy and the communal support they receive may be of prophylactic significance and inhibit symptoms of extreme social deterioration that sometimes accompanies old age. These might be factors in reducing the incidence of severely disturbed behavior among older persons which in the general population often leads to their institutionalization.

The foregoing review of psychotic cases in the Hutterite sect shows an atypical distribution of cases. Functional psychoses accounted for approximately nine out of ten cases, most of whom showed symptoms of manic-depressive reaction, depressed type. The qualitative differences between psychotic patients among the Hutterites and those found in the average American mental hospital are sufficiently pronounced to lend support to the theory that sociological factors are significant in the etiology of psychoses. This theory is further strengthened because certain very general attributes of Hutterite psychotic patients are also found to be common in other forms of mental disorders. They will be further demonstrated in the remaining clinical chapters of this book. They are characteristic of every category of mental disorders in this group. They include:

a. Dominance of depression and introjection of conflicts over acting out or projection;
b. Interpersonal difficulties rather than antisocial problems;
c. Rareness of severe and extreme overt manifestations of psychopathology;
d. Rareness of free-floating anxiety.

7.

Psychoneuroses

MEASURED by the suffering of those affected by them, psychoneuroses are severe mental disorders. Unlike psychotics, psychoneurotic patients do not perceive reality in a grossly distorted manner nor do they present extreme personality disorganization. Their chief characteristic is anxiety. It may be directly felt and expressed, or it may be unconsciously and automatically controlled by the utilization of defense mechanisms such as depression, conversion, displacement, and others. Lifelong studies of such individuals usually present evidence of periodic or chronic maladjustment from childhood on. Many are severely handicapped in living up to the social expectations of their occupation and family status.

Our interest in psychoneurotic cases was a by-product of the concern with psychotic and prepsychotic behavior. We had to look for all symptoms of mental disorder in order to attain maximum completeness in the screening process for psychotic cases. One methodological difficulty in the enumeration of psychoneurotics was the question of selecting a proper cut-off point from normality. At some time all human beings show certain pathological responses which are intense enough to be termed psychoneurotic. We excluded persons with transitory neurotic symptoms under unusual conditions of social or psychological stress. Our case count included only individuals who, in the judgment of the study staff, were or had been a *severe* emotional problem to themselves, their family, or their community. There were 69 such cases. The group, therefore, has a crude lifetime morbidity rate of 8.1 patients per 1,000.

Psychoneurotic cases were enumerated with greater difficulty than psychotic patients. The Hutterites were familiar with psychoses and had their own terminology for some of them. The concept of neurosis was more foreign to them. Our work would have been impossible if it had not been for the intimacy of Hutterite group living. A person with severe neurotic needs usually was a focus of disturbance to himself and others. He was well known. The following five clues were particularly useful. They were frequently associated with cases diagnosed by the staff as psychoneurotic.

1. FREQUENT VISITS TO DOCTORS. Such individuals often were among the first to seek out our staff, particularly the psychiatrist, to discuss their problems. Medical bills shown to the staff by colony leaders, reports from local practitioners, and accounts from Hutterite informants also helped call our attention to such cases.

2. PHYSICAL SYMPTOMS WITHOUT ORGANIC PATHOLOGY. Our staff paid special attention to persons who complained of chronic backaches or headaches, indigestion, constipation, general muscular pain, chronic fatigue, insomnia, hypochondriasis, dysmenorrhea, nervous tics, fainting, frequent nightmares, food allergies, hypertension, and other psychosomatic symptoms. We also looked for evidence of bed-wetting, nail-biting, stuttering, and general restlessness. Persons with such afflictions were often diagnosed as psychoneurotic, but the mere presence of these symptoms was not accepted as sufficient evi-

dence for making a diagnosis. Also considered were the duration of symptoms and their persistence in spite of treatment.

3. FAILURE TO MARRY IN ADULTHOOD. In every colony, special attention was given to persons aged 30 or more who had never married. As was pointed out previously, marriage is very normative in this culture. Eight of the psychoneurotic patients identified in our survey were over 30 and unmarried. They represented 15 per cent of all neurotics, whereas only about four per cent of the normal individuals over 30 were single.

4. INABILITY TO DO A FULL DAY'S WORK. Failure to do a full day's work without positive organic cause was an excellent clue to psychoneurotic problems. All Hutterites are expected to work. Work is important as a prestige factor. Of the 69 psychoneurotic patients, 55, or 80 per cent, were unable to keep up with their normal work, although only one was completely incapacitated during the peak of his illness.

5. RIGIDITY OF ATTITUDE. Some individuals were more rigid in their work expectations or religious orthodoxy than is normal for the Hutterite culture. While the culture makes many demands on its members, no one is expected to work in a hurry, miss out on sleep, or be compulsive about the observance of every minor religious prescription. Many individuals who did show these symptoms were found to be psychoneurotic.

The case count of psychoneurotic Hutterites was probably quite incomplete. The enumerated frequency of cases varied directly, significantly, and in the same direction with the intensity of field work contacts. There were about twice as many adult neurotics in the 19 colonies intensively studied as in the 65 colonies surveyed extensively. The rate of 33 cases per 1,000 persons aged 15 and over established for the intensively studied colonies can be used as a fair estimate of

the true lifetime morbidity of severe psychoneurosis among
Hutterite adults in 1951. Recovered and deceased psychoneurotic patients also were underenumerated. It may be recalled that for psychotics there was no significant change in
the lifetime morbidity rate between 1930 and 1950. As Table
13 shows, the change for psychoneurotic patients was highly
significant.

Table 13—Lifetime Morbidity of Neurosis in the Ethnic Hutterite Population of 1951 and 1930*

Year	Total Population	Number of Cases Ever Ill in Life	Lifetime Morbidity per 1,000 Persons
1950	8,542	69	8.1
1930	3,400	9	2.6
$X^2 = 10.770$			$P = .001$

* The count of cases was completed in the summer of 1951, but the population is based on a census as of December 31, 1950. The population figure for 1930 is an estimate. The case count includes seven persons living in 1951 who were estimated to have been ill at some time before 1930, and two persons dead in 1951 who were living in 1930 and had been ill at or before that time.

Symptomatology

There is more reason for confidence in the general char-
acterization of a person as psychoneurotic than in his differential diagnosis in view of the vagueness and overlapping of
diagnostic criteria. In 34 of the enumerated cases, nearly 50
per cent, there was a multiplicity of symptoms which could
not be classified clearly in any specific category. The diagnosis of *other psychoneurotic reaction* was made. Six patients
showed enough general anxiety about specific problems to
justify the diagnosis of *anxiety reaction*. Most of these cases
also had vague neurasthenic complaints. We did not observe
many symptoms typical of free-floating anxiety. This may
explain the general impression that Hutterite colonies are
populated by relaxed, well-adjusted, and mentally healthy
individuals. It could be expected that free-floating anxiety
would be rare in a culture where the individual has many
close interpersonal relationships and is generally given a

great deal of social and psychological support by his family and his community. A Hutterite usually knows how others will react to something he does. There is little of the deep uncertainty in social relations which is experienced by many people living in a metropolis with widely differing cultural expectations.

Eleven persons were found to have severe depressive symptoms. They were diagnosed as *neurotic-depressive reaction* cases. They had better contact with reality than the psychotic patients diagnosed as suffering from a manic-depressive reaction. Many manic-depressive patients clearly felt well in the interval between depressive moods. The depressive moods of the neurotic patients were more chronic. The neurotic-deprssive persons did not manifest the severe symptoms common to patients with psychotic depression. Delusions, hypochondriac preoccupations, hallucinations, intractable insomnia, suicidal ruminations, motor retardation, profound retardation of thought, and stupor were either absent or relatively mild.

Two female cases diagnosed as *conversion reactions* manifested classical hysterical symptoms. One had a paralysis of the leg and the other had epileptiform fits following a miscarriage.

The remaining sixteen cases were diagnosed as *psychophysiological autonomic and visceral disorders*.* Most of these patients had multiple psychophysiological reactions. Seven of them had predominantly cardiovascular symptoms, five had gastrointestinal reactions, two showed a musculoskeletal condition, and there was one case each of endocrine and nervous reaction. It may be noteworthy that none of the cases had bronchial asthma or colitis.

Most of the patients had chronic neurasthenic and hypo-

---

* This category includes disorders often referred to as psychosomatic disorders or somatization reactions. It should also be noted that girls with dysmenorrhea and persons with milder neurasthenic complaints, who were not generally handicapped by these conditions, were not included in the case count of psychoneurotic patients.

chondriac complaints. They were among the first to seek out our staff to inquire what could be done about their "weak stomachs," low back pain, constipation, high blood pressure, and headaches. They piled up big medical bills for their colony and often had an assortment of medicines in their bedroom. They had run the gamut of medical facilities without receiving relief. They were likely to "try anything," including the brews of a "Chinese Herbalist," a "Lady Gypsy, who seemed to know what she was doing," or a "real doctor from the old country" who could not get a license to practice medicine.

Hutterites did not conceive of neurosis primarily as a mental phenomenon but rather as one involving malfunctioning of an organ or the physical deterioration of the nervous system. Many of the female neurotic patients showed scars of several abdominal operations. In a number of cases, leading local doctors and our staff had doubts about the medical necessity of the operations. Hutterites assign high value to the doctor who provides active treatment. This attitude may have a bearing on the fact that they are more likely to consult a surgeon than a psychiatrist. The existence of serious cultural barriers to adequate communication on mental and emotional problems between Hutterite patients and most of their non-Hutterite doctors can lead to a misinterpretation of the condition by the physician and thus can result in inappropriate medical and surgical treatment methods. This danger is enhanced by the bias of many Hutterites and some of the doctors in their tendency to have more confidence in the therapeutic potentialities of the surgical knife than the psychiatric couch.

It was our impression that neurotic Hutterites react to most stresses with signs of depression rather than with anxiety symptoms or obsessive or paranoid tendencies as neurotic patients often do in the American culture. This rareness of obsessive and compulsive behavior may have something to do with the relative rigidity of the Hutterite culture. Persons who would seem to be compulsive in a loosely structured social system would be more normal in a Hutterite colony, where life is highly regulated by tradition. The Hutterite culture provides such persons with socially approved outlets for compulsiveness. They need only to be orthodox! Some Hutterites were regarded by their community as fanatical in their orthodoxy, but in no case seen by our staff did the psychiatrist think that a diagnosis of compulsive neurotic reaction would be justified. Most members could be relaxed about some of the limits, and all but a few of the compulsions imposed by their way of life. It was not uncommon for people to miss church several evenings without worrying about it. Many of the younger set saw a rodeo show without feeling too much guilt. They discussed such deviations with the statement: "By right we should not do this, but it really is not too bad." They felt secure enough about being good Hutterites to accept something less than 100 per cent submission to the cultural norms. There was some tolerance for the frailties of human nature which did not fit the stereotype of a fundamentalist religious sect. But there was none of the cultural or philosophical relativism which is widespread in the general American population. There was a *right* way for Hutterites to do almost everything, from planning the Sunday breakfast menu to arranging the sleeping quarters in the home. And in most situations Hutterites were able to live up to these normative cultural expectations.

Slightly more than four-fifths of all Hutterite psychoneurotics were women. The predominance of neurotic females was not quite as high as in the Arctic Norwegian village, where only two of the 25 chronically ill neurotics were male! A low sex ratio (fewer neurotic men than women) was also found in the reports of other studies. We do not know what this sex-linkage means. It may have some relation to the social and cultural sex roles. In the patriarchal culture of the Hutterites, men have many more opportunities to externalize aggressive drives and dissatisfactions than do women. The latter may have a greater need to internalize them. It may also have been that a disproportionate number of neurotic women came to the attention of the Hutterite study staff.

Severe neurosis most often manifested itself during adolescence and early adulthood. Almost half of the Hutterite cases clearly showed signs of disturbance between the ages of 15 and 29. This age relationship was more pronounced in women than in men. None of the cases became ill after the age of 50.

Cross-Cultural Comparison

The clinical analysis of psychoneurotic symptoms among Hutterite patients provides support for the theory that cultural and social characteristics were important factors in their etiology. There is a basis for presuming that the Hutterite culture has a bearing on what types of conflicts show up in psychoneurotic patients, the defense mechanisms which are chosen, and the way in which individuals react to anxiety. A quantitative approach to this problem is more difficult. Although we shall present the data we have, the epidemiological method is less rewarding than was true of psychoses. Psychoneurotic diagnostic categories are less clear-cut.

Population surveys varied greatly in efforts that could be devoted to the enumeration of cases of psychoneurosis, including those where a recovery had taken place. Psychoneurotic patients were enumerated in five of the populations, but the criteria for case counting varied greatly. The published reports provide insufficient information about the standards used to distinguish between symptoms diagnosed as psychoneurotic and the neurotic manifestations inherent in everyday living. The standard expectancy method, which was applied in the epidemiological analysis of psychosis, cannot be used to make a comparison of psychoneuroses, because valid age- or sex-specific rates of psychoneuroses do not exist for any population. Some of the bias introduced by the extremely youthful composition of the Hutterites can be reduced by eliminating children from the cross-cultural comparison.

The Arctic Norwegian Village study reported the highest frequency. Johan Bremer found 60 cases in which "constitutional dispositions have yielded in relation to acute or chronic pressure of the environment and in which the symptoms are not of a psychotic nature."[72] The enumeration of cases was restricted to those who became ill during a five year period. Approximately 40 per cent of the patients were classified as chronic. The remaining 60 per cent were diagnosed as transient cases of psychoneurosis because they showed relatively mild neurasthenic and hypochondriac symptoms. The prevalence rate of psychoneurosis in the community during the five year period ending in 1944 was approximately 64 per 1,000, aged 15 and over. In addition there were 22 individuals, or approximately 23 cases per 1,000, aged 15 and over, who suffered from "war neurosis." The village was subjected to air bombardment and the population experienced considerable stress as a result of its occupation by German troops.

The Hutterites had a lower frequency of psychoneurosis. The enumerated lifetime morbidity rate, including active and recovered cases, was 16.4 per 1,000, aged 15 and over. In Hutterite colonies that were surveyed intensively, the rate was twice as great. Approximately 25 per cent of the psychoneurotic patients were diagnosed as recovered.

The Formosa area had by far the lowest frequency: 2.1 psychoneurotics per 1,000, aged 15 and over.[73] This report made no distinction between active and recovered cases, and may not have included too many of the latter. Williamson County, Tennessee, and the Baltimore Eastern Health districts respectively reported prevalence rates of 5.7 and 4.0

per 1,000, aged 15 and over.[74] Their case counts were restricted to active cases.

In general the rank order of these crude morbidity rates was the same as that found in psychoses. (See Table 10, page 55.) However, the variations of the five surveys in methods of diagnosis, case counting, and effectiveness of screening procedures were so great that the validity of this conclusion is very uncertain. In all areas, with perhaps the exception of the Arctic Norwegian Village, the true frequency of psychoneurosis was probably considerably above the enumerated frequency.

All these rates of adult neurotic illness were low when compared with short-term incidence rates of factory workers. The latter were obtained by Russell Fraser, who made medical observations on 2,000 male and female British workers in a clinic setting over a period of six months. He reported that during the course of six months 10 per cent suffered from an active disabling neurotic illness and a further 20 per cent from minor forms of neurosis. These findings were in keeping with previous estimates of the extent of neurotic illness among factory workers.[75]

The interpretation of these quantitative findings must be very tentative. It is probable that some of the large variations in the enumerated frequency of psychoneurosis reflect true differences in the susceptibility of the various populations. The Hutterite sect probably has significantly fewer psychoneurotic members than groups who live under unusually stressful social conditions, such as the inhabitants of the Arctic Norwegian Village or inhabitants of American urban areas. However, the presence of a considerable number of severely psychoneurotic individuals, perhaps as many as one out of every thirty adults, in this fairly protective and cohesive social system indicates that their culture, as was true of functional psychoses, also provides no immunity from this form of functional disorder. There may be genetic and constitutional factors which predispose some people in all human groups to react to stress with psychoneurotic symptoms; there certainly is no social system without some of the social and cultural conflicts which seem to be associated with psychoneurosis. However, the good mental health which has been ascribed to Hutterites by those who have observed them is not entirely contradicted by this finding. The sect probably does have a fairly low frequency of psychoneurotic disorders. What may be even more significant from the point of view of mental health, most Hutterite patients have fairly mild and benign symptoms. They are able to function in their communities and families with considerable acceptance for the limitations imposed by their psychoneurotic difficulties upon their social functioning.

Cultural values and social relations are far more widely accepted as significant factors for the etiology of psychoneuroses than of psychoses. In the latter category, genetic and organic factors are given somewhat more emphasis. These theoretical assumptions are based on the hypothesis that psychoses and psychoneuroses involve different disease processes. Among the Hutterites, the onset of psychoses tended to be more sudden than that of psychoneuroses. Psychoneurotic symptoms also seemed to be more chronic than were most functional psychotic disorders, particularly the manic-depressive reactions. About twice as many of the Hutterite psychotic patients were diagnosed as recovered as were psychoneurotic individuals.

A different theory, that psychoses and psychoneuroses are *alternate* manifestations of the *same* disease process, appears at least doubtful on the basis of our findings. The enumerated frequencies of neurotic and psychotic symptoms in the five populations were not inversely related to each other. The Hutterite ratio of psychoneurotic to psychotic patients was 1.30. In the population with the highest frequency of psychoses, the Arctic Norwegian Village, the number of psychoneurotics was even greater, relatively and absolutely. The ratio of the two disorders was 1.58 or, if the war neurosis cases are included in the category of psychoneuroses, 2.32. In the Formosa area, where the frequency of psychoses was lower than in any other population reviewed in this book, the number of psychoneuroses was not only small, but even smaller than the frequency of psychoses. The ratio of the two disorders was 0.32.* This observation also might raise doubt about the interesting suggestion of Jacob Schwartz and Elvin V. Semrad that psychosomatic disorders which are among those enumerated as psychoneuroses in our comparison study ". . . are in a sense a defense and protection against psychotic break—that to a certain extent an 'either (psychosomatic) or (psychotic)' mechanism may prevail."[76] Some of these frequency variations and ratios were without a doubt an accidental consequence of research methodology and intensity of screening, but the differences were sufficiently great to justify asking questions about their possible etiological significance.

Emotional Problems in Children

The growing Hutterite child is molded consciously and consistently by parents, teachers, and the impact of all community institutions. The goal of this fairly rigid and deterministic socialization process is the making of an adult who will live in conformity with the expectations of the Hutterite way of life. Impulsive behavior in children—for example, masturbation and aggression—which is regarded as "normal" by most contemporary child-rearing experts, is energetically repressed. Permissiveness in child rearing is not a Hutterite virtue; it is regarded as a vice.

Just as iron tends to rust and as the soil will nourish weeds,

---

* The ratio of the two disorders was 0.36 in Baltimore and 0.63 in Tennessee.

unless it is kept clean by continuous care, so have the children of men a strong inclination towards injustices, desires and lusts; especially when the children are together with the children of the world and daily hear and see their bad examples. In consequence they desire nothing but dancing, playing and all sorts of frivolities, till they have such a longing for it, that you cannot stop them any more from growing up in it. . . . Now it has been revealed that many parents are by nature too soft with their children and have not the strength to keep them away from evil. So we have a thousand good reasons why we should live separated from the world in a Christian community. How much misery is prevented in this way! For do we not hear it often said: How honest and respectable are these people; but look what godless children they brought up! Some show a damnable insolence, others are un-Christian drinkers, and some are given to frivolous playing and dancing. Sometimes father and mother have died long ago and nothing is left of their earthly remains, but their bad reputation still lives among the people who complain that they once neglected to discipline their children and brought them up disgracefully.

   We see this on the terrible example of the priest Eli, who himself led an irreproachable life, but neglected the education of his godless sons. So God the Lord became angry and announced it to Eli through a man of God, that he would expel his whole family from the priesthood and exterminate them root and branch. (1 Sam. 2.) And in the end, when you read on several chapters, it was fulfilled; for not only Eli and his own family, but also all Israel came to utter ruin, and Eli died a sudden death and his sons perished. (1 Sam. 4, 15-22). The enemies captured the ark of God, the seat of his glory, Israel was beaten and the whole city of Nobe was put to the sword, including the women, children and infants.[77]

These clear-cut and portentous admonitions against permissiveness and relativism in child rearing were written in 1652 by the Hutterite elder, Andreas Erenpreis. In theory, they guide the thinking of contemporary Hutterites about education and childhood indoctrination, although a diffusion of more permissive contemporary educational philosophies can be observed in some families and communities.

The psychological impact on children of these cultural values regarding education could not be studied with the intensity which this problem deserves, but some preliminary findings can be reported here. No severe habit disturbances and antisocial behavior were found in any of the 131 youngsters who were medically screened by the psychiatrist and about whom a record was kept by our staff. The findings were equally negative for at least another 200 children, who were examined without a record being kept. Of the adult patients diagnosed as psychoneurotic, only six estimated that their illness had begun between the ages of 10 and 14. Hutterite leaders and parents, who generally were quite free in sharing with our staff any knowledge they had about adults who were psychotic or otherwise mentally ill, did not call our attention to a single child whom they regarded as a severe psychiatric problem. This finding can be contrasted with the observation of Johan Bremer that not less than one-fourth of the children aged 5-14 in the Arctic Norwegian Village were maladjusted. In the Eastern Health District of Baltimore, Lemkau and his collaborators enumerated 140 children with neurotic traits among 10,636 between the ages of 6 and 16, a rate of 13.2 per 1,000. A. R. Mangus[78] found many poorly adjusted youngsters in his mental health study of rural children, although none of his subjects were given a psychiatric diagnosis.

Our staff noted children with habit disturbances, such as nail-biting, enuresis, and thumb-sucking. There were also conduct problems like temper tantrums, quarrelsomeness, disobedience, untruthfulness, and what would be thought of as "cruelty to animals" in an urban setting. These behavior deviations were not, however, regarded as major problems by Hutterite adults. All children tend to rebel against restrictions; they get scolded or spanked to "learn to mind." Tears were not infrequent in Hutterite kindergartens or schools; they were regarded as a necessary evil. Several non-Hutterite public school teachers were asked by the parents not to spare the rod. The parents explained: "How else are they to learn to live right?"

Few Hutterite children become so severely disturbed as to require the intervention of parents, the community, or medical men, but childhood is a period of considerable psychological stress. This conclusion is inferred from the results of a battery of paper-pencil tests designed to measure "emotional adjustment." The tests were administered by superintendents of public schools, at our request, to 415 Hutterite youngsters and their teachers. They were given in the schools of 36 colonies. Most of the children were between 9 and 15 years of age. For 306 of them additional ratings were obtained from Hutterite religious teachers.* The ratings were made on a five point scale. The results were summarized in Table 14 by combining as plus (+) the strongly and mildly positive, as minus (−) the strongly and mildly negative, and as neutral the children not rated or rated as average from the point of view of mental health.

Both Hutterite and public school teachers characterized a surprisingly large proportion of their charges as "poorly adjusted." "Tendency towards depression" was the most common negative judgment. Two-thirds of the children were so rated by the public school teachers; the Hutterite teachers included more than four in five of their pupils in this category. Despite these negative opinions, the teachers of colonies visited by our staff failed to call our attention to any child with severe behavior problems, although they referred us to mentally defective and epileptic youngsters.

One factor in this predominantly negative picture was the psychological outlook of the teachers. For many, a "good"

---

* The teacher-rating instrument was adapted from the "Rating Scale for Pupil Adjustment" developed by the Michigan Department of Mental Health, State of Michigan, Lansing, Michigan, under the direction of Dr. Ralph E. Walton, who graciously gave permission to use it.

Table 14—Summary of Personal Adjustment Ratings of Hutterite School Children by Public School and Hutterite Religious Teachers Using the Michigan Rating Scale for Pupil Adjustment

| | DIRECTION OF RATINGS IN PERCENTAGE | | | | | |
| | N = 415 Children Public School Teachers | | | N = 306 Children Hutterite Teachers | | |
	(—)	(0)	(+)	(—)	(0)	(+)
1. Over-all Emotional Adjustment (Definition: Total emotional adequacy in meeting the daily problems of living as manifested in school.)	50.4	39.0	10.6	66.4	26.8	6.8
2. Social Maturity (Definition: Ability to deal with social responsibilities in school, in the community, and at home, appropriate to the pupil's age.)	29.9	54.5	15.6	44.1	50.3	5.6
3. Tendency Towards Depression (Definition: Tendency towards melancholia, depressed mood reaction.)	67.7	24.8	7.5	81.4	17.3	1.3
4. Tendency Towards Aggressive Behavior (Definition: Overt evidence of hostility and/or aggression towards other children and/or adults.)	65.1	24.8	10.1	60.4	35.9	3.7
5. Extroversion - Introversion (Definition: Tendency towards living outwardly and expressing emotions spontaneously (+) vs. tendency towards living inwardly and keeping emotions to himself (—).)	29.4	54.2	16.4	33.6	54.3	12.1
6. Emotional Security (Definition: Feeling of being accepted by and friendly towards one's environment.)	66.5	27.7	5.8	74.5	24.5	1.0
7. Motor Control and Stability (Definition: Capacity for effective co-ordination and control of motor activity of the entire body.)	59.8	34.9	5.3	65.0	31.4	3.6
8. Impulsiveness (Definition: Tendency towards sudden or marked changes of mood.)	41.4	39.3	19.3	56.9	37.6	5.5

Table 14—(Continued)

9. Emotional Irritability (Definition: Tendency to become angry, irritated, or upset.)	55.2	31.6	13.2	61.1	36.0	2.9
10. School Achievement (Definition: Overall evaluation of pupil's competency in school subjects relative to his own age group.)	33.7	44.4	21.9	51.9	40.9	7.2
11. School Conduct (Definition: Conduct in the classroom situation as evidence of ability to accept the rules and regulations of the school community.)	35.4	52.8	11.8	52.3	43.8	3.9

child was a submissive youngster. Many objected to spontaneity and reacted to it with disciplinary measures. This generalization applied most strongly to Hutterite teachers. Nevertheless, Hutterite teachers thought that only 4 per cent of the children disliked them; public school teachers said this was true of 12 per cent of their pupils.

The teachers also were asked to check certain indices of physical, emotional, and intellectual development. The public school teachers were somewhat more sensitive to the psychological items; the Hutterite teachers checked a larger proportion of physical items, although many of the differences are not significant. Both agreed that there were many children who had problems. The results are summarized in Table 15.

The contradiction between the frequently negative ratings of Hutterite children by their teachers and the failure on the part of our staff to enumerate children with severe behavior disturbances may be related to the fact that the screening of children was less intensive than of adults. However, at least some, and probably much, of the contrast can be explained as a difference in cultural norms or expectations between the study staff and the Hutterites. A youngster who was without signs of severe psychological pathology or disabling psychosomatic symptoms was diagnosed as "normal" by the staff, although his behavior might have been judged as quite "poor" by the standards of his teachers. A Hutterite youngster does not have to burn a barn, expose his genitals, or run away from home to be a "problem" child. A little youthful exuberance will be sufficient. An incident that occurred during our field work may be related to illustrate this point. A young staff member, who is very spontaneous with children, started to

Table 15—Rating of Hutterite School Children by American (or Canadian) Public School and Hutterite Religious Teachers

Item to Be Rated	PERCENTAGE OF CHILDREN RATED "YES"	
	N = 415 Children Public School Teachers	N = 305 Children Hutterite Teachers
1. The child's parents are poor educators.	18.3	2.3
2. The child is quite nervous.	15.2	4.9
3. The child is quite dull mentally.	10.4	5.2
4. The child has frequent headaches.	8.2	3.6
5. The child bites his nails.	14.0	10.1
6. The child cries quite often.	3.9	0.7
7. The child has a speech handicap	5.5	3.6
8. The child is unusually tall for his age.	8.9	23.5
9. The child is a leader in the class.	19.8	30.1
10. I think the child likes me.	73.7	81.4
11. The child is markedly overweight.	1.9	6.9
12. The child is unusually short for his age.	8.0	11.8
13. The child is quite bright mentally.	55.4	59.2
14. The child has poor digestion.	0.7	2.6
15. The child is not well liked by other children.	6.5	7.8
16. The child is unusually underweight or anemic.	5.5	6.2

play tag with a group that had gathered around him. The tagging progressed into hitting, and our field worker was soon preoccupied warding off shouting boys and girls who were competing in the effort to get a lick at him. The staff member enjoyed the "game" and encouraged it. Suddenly the shrill voice of an elderly lady came out of an entrance door of the communal kitchen across the courtyard: "*Geht*

Heim!" (Go home!). As if hit by lightning, the children froze, stopped, and dispersed. One remark from a respected adult was enough to curb them, although the woman was not the parent of any of them. Later, she and several other adults apologized profusely to the staff member for the behavior of the youngsters explaining: "They are awfully bad."

The rareness of severe emotional pathology in view of these practices may have something to do with the fact that most parents and some of the teachers give children more than discipline. They also show much love. The culture encourages parents to be permissive towards the physical and intellectual limitations of children at various stages of development. There is a fairly positive emotional identification even with those youngsters who are defective. Children are the only wealth an adult may call his own. There are few competing values, no professional ambitions or compulsive status aspirations. Gross neglect, of the kind that would bring an urban child to the attention of school or police authorities, is virtually impossible in this group.

The traumatic impact of suppression of the spontaneity of children by adults may also be lessened by the strong horizontal identification among youngsters in the same age groups. No child is singled out for restriction or punishment. It is an experience shared by all. Youngsters are greatly influenced by those a few years older, with whom they spend more time than with adults. Hutterite children learn in easy stages to identify with the adult role.

The pupils agree, at least to some extent, with the opinion of teachers that they have many emotional problems as they grow up. This fact is aparent from the analysis of the SRA Youth Inventory,* a modified version of which was in-

---

* Adapted with permission of Dr. H. H. Remmers, one of the orig-inators of the test. Dr. A. J. Drucker and Miss E. Sjostedt, a student work-ing under his direction, analyzed some of the test responses and made their results available to us.

cluded in the objective test battery. The children were asked
to check which of 229 items applied to them. While there
were many difficulties in the interpretation of the test results,*
it is probably noteworthy that 404 Hutterite school children
who completed the SRA Inventory checked significantly
more problems than the national United States sample upon
whom the test was standardized. For example, Hutterite
youngsters were very much concerned with learning to control themselves. Their responses were high to such statements as "I have difficulties keeping my mind on my studies"
(56 per cent); "I must learn not to get excited when things
go wrong" (64 per cent); "I am trying to get rid of an undesirable habit" (56 per cent). There also was considerable evidence of guilt and a preoccupation with living up to community expectation. "I feel guilty about things I have done"
(61 per cent); "I often do things I later regret" (56 per cent);
"I want people to like me better" (60 per cent); "I want
to make new friends" (76 per cent); "I need to learn how to
be a good sport" (60 per cent); "Does it really pay to be
honest?" (76 per cent); and "Is it right to deny the existence
of God?" (58 per cent). Some of the responses, which in
the Amercian culture might be evidence of personal maladjustment, probably have a different meaning for Hutterites.
Their "yes" responses showed an awareness of reality, which
most youngsters can accept as "normal": "I need to learn how
to order food in a restaurant" (48 per cent); "I have no way
of earning my own spending money" (43 per cent); "My
parents are trying to decide my job for me" (41 per cent).

---

* As many as 40 per cent of the youngsters gave an indication that
they checked some questions indiscriminately. There are difficulties even
in the same culture in applying to one social group a psychological test
standardized in another. These problems are compounded when such
an instrument is used in a culture where children are subjected to a very
different socialization process. Similar difficulties in the use of American
psychological test norms with Hutterites were observed by W. W. Ludeman and J. R. McAnelly.[79]

Culture and Psychoneurosis

The frequency and severity of psychoneurotic symptoms in a population are probably strongly affected by their social relations and cultural values. John Dollard and Neal E. Miller[80] have pointed out that psychoneuroses involve learned behaviors, which are reinforced by environmental influences. The Hutterite data fit this theory well. Adult patients in this group had chiefly those neurotic symptoms which were socially acceptable in their culture. They took their tensions out on themselves by internalizing them as depressive or psychophysiological responses. Phobic and obsessive compulsive reactions, which would violate strong cultural taboos, were rare. Within their highly structured social system, individuals also were sufficiently sheltered and guided to make generalized anxiety reactions rare. If this socio-cultural learning theory is applicable to psychoneuroses, Hutterites should manifest different and perhaps more psychoneurotic reactions as they become acculturated to the larger American society.

This theory also was supported by the finding that severe behavior disorders were uncommon among Hutterite youngsters, although there were many emotional problems in children which were recognized by them and their teachers. Children were generally wanted, they experienced a great deal of affection and acceptance by parents and most other people in a colony, but they were subject to a great deal of rigid and consistent discipline. The Hutterite failure to bring childhood problems to the attention of the field staff, although they freely co-operated in giving the writers access to mental disorder cases, may have been related to certain basic Hutterite assumptions about children. Adults who had an emotional or psychoneurotic problem required recognition from the community because they created problems in the personal and work relationships of the colony. Children were not regarded as full-fledged members. Their difficulties were not appropriate matters for action by the entire group. They were of concern only to the parents and the Hutterite teacher. While adults were expected to adjust fully to community standards, children were not. It was expected that they would have some difficulties in curbing their impulses and in learning to accept the restrictions that are inherent in being a Hutterite. Adults noted psychological symptoms like temper tantrums and shyness, but they did not regard them as pathological. They tended to dismiss them with the thought: "They'll grow out of it." Parents and the school developed a routine for handling these situations, which simply do not become problems requiring special community intervention unless there are dramatic symptoms. This attitude is all the more understandable in a group in which the median completed family has more than ten children. Hutterite youngsters are important to their parents, but they cannot be the center of much individual attention. An eight-year-old Hutterite boy, who wets his bed, is thought to be "someone who wets his bed when he is too old for that." He may even be taken to a doctor to see if a pill can be prescribed that would help him. But he is no "problem." A middle-class boy of an urban American family would be likely to be thought of as having a "problem." He would be brought to the attention of a doctor or guidance counsellor, who might make a diagnosis of habit disorder. Adult informants who spoke freely about their current personal problems generally gave amazingly stereotyped and emotionally impoverished accounts of their childhood period, which was only a few steps removed from childhood amnesia. They probably had at least as many emotional problems as their children have today. Nevertheless our data indicate that it may be possible to submit children in this relatively integrated social system to severely restrictive and disciplinary experiences without producing pathological reactions of the severity seen daily in child guidance centers in urban areas.

8.

Personality Disorder and
Social Disorganization

THE HUTTERITTE reputation for mental health was clearly confirmed in one respect. There were few cases of personality disorder. This category of illness is ". . . characterized by developmental defects or pathological trends in the personality structure, with minimal subjective anxiety and little or no sense of distress. In most instances, the disorder is manifested by life-long patterns of action or behavior, rather than by mental or emotional symptoms."[81] Among the symptoms are antisocial acts by persons who are amoral, without a conscience, unable to take roles of others, ineffective in their communications, and incapable of learning very much from experience. Personality disorder is no doubt the vaguest of all concepts in the psychiatric nomenclature. But it describes what is perhaps the most critical of all mental disorders because of their severely disturbing consequences for society. A high frequency of such individuals would threaten the very existence of the social order far more than an equal number of psychotic, psychoneurotic, or mentally defective patients.

Personality disorders cannot be clearly differentiated from unusual or antisocial acts of "normal" persons. Kirson S. Weinberg, who reviews the recent literature in this field, explains that the ". . . lack of agreement concerning these disorders is so prevalent that one of our purposes is to point out and to clarify the sources of this confusion."[82] He illustrates this point well by reference to the survey in the Eastern Health District of Baltimore. There, 1.3 per 1,000 population were diagnosed as psychopathic personalities in 1933. In a second survey in 1936 the figure was cut down to 0.5. In 1936 a change in standards by the social workers resulted in a different diagnosis for many of the unemployed persons who had been regarded as psychopaths in 1933, when unemployment was considered by some to be evidence of personal failure rather than a social catastrophe. The line between having a personality disorder and being a victim of social disorganization is thin.

There seemed to be no serious, and only a few petty, violations of moral norms by Hutterites, although every effort was made by our staff to find all severe personality disorder cases and instances of socially deviant behavior. Observations made by previous investigators on this subject were generally confirmed. One of them was Bertha W. Clark, who reported in 1924:

Huterian [sic] communities are and always have been particularly free from vice and crime, as they are also from poverty. There have never been cases of murder, arson, burglary, forgery, rioting among them, their social and economic life having been put on such a basis that such things naturally have not developed. They have no policemen, nor ever call on those of the outside world. There is no Huterian [sic] person in a jail or prison, in an almshouse or orphan asylum, or in any institution supported by public moneys, excepting only the schools. . . .[83]

Lee Emerson Deets also observed in 1939 that "Crime, against our society or their own is very rare."[84] We found four Hutterites with symptoms of personality disorders and two young men who stuttered mildly but were otherwise well adjusted socially. (Speech disturbances are also classified as "Personality Disorders" in the American Psychiatric Association *Statistical Manual.*) The lifetime morbidity rate was 0.9 per 1,000, aged 15 and over, or 1.4 if the stutterers were included. In contrast, Fremming estimated that three per cent of the total population of Denmark was psychopathic on the basis of the surveys made by him and Strömgren on the Island of Bornholm.[85] In seven of the ten populations, personality dis-

Table 16—Lifetime Morbidity of Personality Disorders Enumerated in Seven Census Type Studies

Population and Type of Diagnostic Category	Number of Cases Enumerated	Rate per 1,000 Population, Aged 15 and Over
Ethnic Hutterites		
Personality Disorders	4	0.9
Formosa Area		
Psychopathic Personality	18	1.6
Alcoholism	2	0.2
Thuringia Villages*		
Psychopaths	25	0.9
Eccentrics	6	0.2
Alcoholics	15	0.5
Bavarian Villages*		
Psychopaths	5	2.1
Alcoholics	5	2.1
Debility	36	15.6
West Swedish Island		
Psychopaths	2	3.1
Williamson County, Tennessee		
Psychopathic Traits	152	8.8
Special Personality Types	208	12.0
Arctic Norwegian Village		
Asthenic	28	30.0
Depression	6	6.5
Weak Willed	51	54.8
Explosive	5	5.4
Emotionally Labile	3	3.2
Querulous	2	2.2
"Eccentric"	6	6.5
Total Psychopathic	101	108.6

* Rates per 1,000, aged 16 and over.

order frequencies were reported, often in categories like psychopath or alcoholic. The findings are summarized in Table 16. In all the areas personality disorder cases were more common than among the Hutterites.

The four true Hutterite personality disorder cases presented chronic social problems to their community. One engaged in antisocial acts that required intervention by police authorities. He repeatedly stole colony property to buy liquor and cigarettes; he was jailed twice for such offenses. The second case was a leader in his colony, a mild alcoholic, who gambled, misused colony funds, and chronically violated many other mores of the culture. So far he managed to retain his position of leadership through being cautious and adept at political machinations which would be appropriate in Tammany Hall in New York. The third case was a religiously compulsive older woman, and the fourth, an emotionally unstable and negativistic housewife, who was critical of everything. Both of the females frequently were the center of acrimony. None of these cases could be characterized as severe. While none would require institutionalization in our culture, the prognosis for their improvement or recovery was not good. Their life history showed a consistent pattern of social disorientation.

Hutterites were generally quite unsympathetic towards these persons. Neither the devil nor "sickness of mind" nor an organic cause was believed to be operating, as was true of other forms of mental disorder. The personality disorders were regarded as an exercise of "bad" will by the individual. The people affected were a common topic of gossip. There was little reticence to discuss these "black sheep," as they were commonly termed. It is doubtful that many severe cases were missed. Neurotic patients had few symptoms that raised differential diagnostic questions in the direction of a diagnosis of personality disorder. However, our survey did not screen persons with occasional mild tendencies towards this disorder.

Crime Among the Hutterites

During the first six months of 1952, according to the *Uniform Crime Reports* issued by the Federal Bureau of Investigation, the incidence of major crimes in all reporting rural areas was 2.6 offenses per 1,000 inhabitants.[86] These reports covered only *severe* crimes like murder, manslaughter, rape, robbery, assault, burglary, larceny, and auto theft. Hutterites were virtually free from crime if judged by this standard. We did not find a single case of murder, assault, or rape. Physical aggressiveness of any sort was quite rare. Children were taught early not to fight with each other. Teachers reported that before their youngsters left school at the age of 15, they had learned this cultural doctrine well. They might get angry, but words were their only weapon. Fighting among adults was severely frowned upon. Physical aggression was approved of only against children for disciplinary purposes.

There were only petty law violations. Twelve Hutterites were known to have served time in a jail for stealing, but they were generally one-time offenders. Four persons ran afoul of the law for selling wine, a beverage made by all colonies for home use and rationed to each adult on a monthly quota basis. A youngster also spent a short period in jail for trapping without a license. Most of the offenders were young men who wanted to have more spending money than the colonies give individuals for their own use; the allowance is never more than a dollar a month and much less in some colonies. In about two-thirds of the cases, they returned to their community. Several rose to positions of leadership as they grew older. "They learned their lesson," many informants would explain, and some were described as being "stronger in their faith than the rest of us."

We restricted the enumeration of violations of property mores to those reported to the police. There were additional instances of petty stealing by members, particularly from their own colony. Probably no Hutterite adult goes through life without occasionally making unauthorized use of colony property. Such violations take several forms. Some men cheat a little on their expense account to cover the cost of an extra glass of beer. Young boys who want money to buy a special present for their girl friends may work for private gain for a neighbor when they are not needed in the group. In one colony with weak leadership, there were reports that men conducting business for the colony had asked for kick-back presents. In many colonies trapping animals to sell fur during the winter has almost become accepted as a legitimate private enterprise, even though it contradicts the general Hutterite philosophy that all earnings must be shared. In general, violations of the strict Hutterite regulations regarding the use of colony property are not common; but they do occur. They are normally well under control through church discipline and group pressure.

The generally favorable record of Hutterites regarding theft from outsiders runs counter to strongly prevailing opinions in some of the towns near which Hutterite colonies are located. Our staff was told by a few of the townspeople that Hutterites "steal anything they can get their hands on." These rumors were more a reflection of how these outsiders felt about the unusual features of the Hutterite way of life than they were accurate reports. Most of these rumors, when we were able to trace them to their source, turned out to have no validity. A Hutterite youngster's pocketing of a candy bar, or a mistake by a Hutterite *boss* in adding a column of figures, can start a rumor about a "Hutterite Crime Wave" which may last for years.

The accuracy of our findings regarding officially recorded crimes is supported by many reports from police authorities in response to our inquiries. One Canadian provincial law enforcement officer wrote: "I can say from my personal experience that while these people live in colonies, they are free from crime and juvenile delinquency." An American county official sent the following report, which we paraphrase at length because it gives an excellent account of both the hostility which Hutterites have encountered in some areas and their relationships to the law:

There are several colonies in this county, each of which has rather extensive holdings on some of the choicest agricultural land, the possession of which has led to considerable feelings against them by other residents and land-owners. This feeling has manifested itself in prior years by public meetings held in different parts of the county, denouncing the movement and further expansion of the organization, the destruction of one of their barns by incendiarism and other numerous though less serious acts against them.

In spite of all this, and with no personal sympathy or liking for their organization, I must report that their criminal and civil records are above average.

Our findings are similar for other socially disapproved behavior. As has been noted previously, no Hutterite child has ever been known to suffer neglect requiring the intervention by either Hutterite or government officials. The same applies to the aged, the sick, and the infirm. No Hutterite has ever been allowed to become a public charge as long as he wished to remain a member of his community. Marriages are remarkably stable. Only one divorce and four separations are known to have occurred in the history of the group in America.

Sex Deviations

No Hutterite has been involved in a sex crime which came to the attention of the authorities. We know of no act of overt homosexuality. Some isolated violations of the strict sex mores of this group have come to our attention, but their frequency is negligible if the Kinsey reports on human sex behavior are accepted as a point of reference.[87] There is information about ten illegitimate babies which may have been born during the last two or three decades. Four Hutterites are known to have had sexual relations with "outsiders." In one case there is evidence that a Hutterite girl was made pregnant by a non-Hutterite. This young woman left her colony and married the man involved. We may have missed some cases of transgression of Hutterite sex mores, for our staff discussed this topic with only a few persons in each area. We were careful to avoid giving the impression to any of our informants that our study of mental health was focused on this topic, although sex attitudes and behavior are important aspects of psychodynamics.

Violations of Hutterite Mores

In every group, deviant behavior must be judged by the standards of the group's culture. Among the Hutterites a person who likes to smoke is thought to have a vice, and he is likely to view himself in such a light. We therefore looked for people who were "problems" because of their difficulties in living up to the severe and rigid expectations of their sect. We restricted the enumeration of cases to two of the most serious Hutterite "wrongs": serving in the armed forces of the United States or Canada, and leaving one's colony to live "in private, on the outside." Both acts are symptomatic of considerable rejection of the Hutterite culture. They are regarded as "awful" by every good member, even though the outside American culture evaluates these acts quite otherwise.

A Hutterite who serves in an army is violating Jesus' admonition against violence. To some Hutterites, a soldier is almost a murderer. He invites on himself eternal damnation. A person who leaves the colony also purchases a ticket to hell because he "refuses to live in community as did Christ and his apostles." However, the group is nearly always ready to receive a sinner back with no more than a token ritual punishment—excommunication for a number of days or weeks. "Deserters," as Hutterites call those who leave, are welcome to visit their families, even for extended periods. Hutterites are far more tolerant towards these deviants than might be expected from their theological point of view. The deviants are hardly ever rejected as persons. Family ties are maintained and often succeed in bringing the "stray lamb back to the fold." Hope is never given up, unless the deserter marries an "outsider." We know of only one case among the 24 men and three women who left their village to marry a non-Hutterite in which the wife agreed to join the sect.*

Table 17 gives a breakdown of the 258 Hutterite men and 11 women who left their colony voluntarily at some time. More than half of them returned.† Most left between the age of 15 and 29. Many Hutterite adults told our staff they had given some thought to leaving when they were young, without ever taking the step. Some of the men who were enumerated as permanent deserters in 1951 have returned since the completion of our field work. It is probable that the proportion of Hutterite males who have left and will never return to their colony is somewhat less than five per cent. For females permanent departure is very rare.

On the basis of the information at our disposal, it may be said that all but a few of these deserters adjusted well. Most of those over 30 were married. They were generally law-abiding, joined a fundamentalist Protestant church, and supported themselves as farmers, laborers, and semiskilled craftsmen. None were known to have attained prominence as leaders or notoriety as social problem cases. Our acquaintance with these ex-Hutterites is far less adequate than it is for regular members, but we doubt that many severe cases

---

* This family lived in a colony which is not in good standing with the Hutterite church because its members are not sufficiently orthodox.

† There were also 276 men who, as conscientious objectors, were required by law to serve in C.O. camps during World War II. They were about one-third of all men living in 1950 who were between the ages of 15 and 35 in 1940. Only four of these conscientious objectors chose to separate themselves from the sect. All others had returned by 1951.

of personality adjustment among these "deserters" escaped our screening process.

Culture, Personality Disorders, and Antisocial Acts

Human beings have many ways of reacting to stress. We have shown in previous chapters that Hutterites tend to internalize or somatize rather than project or act out their difficulties. This principle is most apparent when the frequency of personality disorders and antisocial acts is considered. There were few symptoms of acting out tensions in a socially harmful manner. This finding supports the theory that the prevention of antisocial behavior is possible in some social and cultural settings.

In general, Hutterites were exceedingly effective in rearing their children to live up to the basic moral principles which they share with the larger society. Their integrated system of belief was taught energetically to every member

Table 17—The Frequency of Voluntary Long-Term Departure of Hutterites from Their Colonies

| Type of Absence | AGE AT LEAVING | | | | | |
	15-19	20-24	25-29	30+	Unknown	Total
Male						
Permanent deserters	29	18	7	7	45	106*
Female						
Permanent deserters	0	2	1	0	5	8
Male						
Temporary deserters who returned	16	39	18	27	41	141†
Female						
Temporary deserters who returned	1	1	0	0	1	3
Men who volunteered in the armed services of the U.S. or Canada	2	5	1	1	17	26

* Three permanent deserters also were conscientious objectors. Fourteen others served in the armed service. A few of the permanent deserters left many decades ago and no longer maintain any contact with their families.

† One male deserted his colony. Later he joined the armed services and then returned to his colony.

of the society. Most people acquired a strong superego to inhibit and suppress antisocial impulses. This inner control was reinforced by social pressure. There was a high degree of agreement among the Hutterites about what is "right" and what is "wrong."

Many students of human behavior, under the influence of Sigmund Freud, attribute the faulty operations of social structures to the failures of social control over man's primitive and self-seeking biological drives. Freud expressed much doubt of the existence of a social order in which humanity's aggressive tendencies can be suppressed:

In some happy corners of the earth, they say, where nature brings forth abundantly whatever man desires, there flourish races whose lives go gently by, unknowing of aggression or constraint. This I can hardly credit; I would like further details about these happy folk.[88]

The pessimism of Freud stems from his theoretical orientation, which emphasizes the psychodynamic factor in human behavior. In one respect our findings confirm his theoretical approach. Antisocial impulses were present in all Hutterites about whom we have psychological data. This fact is particularly evident in the analysis of projective tests, administered by our staff and analyzed by Bert Kaplan and Thomas Plaut.[89] The Thematic Apperception Test responses of Hutterites were rich in stories involving personal violence, murder, and stealing. The potentiality for antisocial behavior was found in almost every respondent who took these and other projective tests. But these tendencies were not acted out overtly and directly.

The fact that overt antisocial behavior and the use of violence are rare in the Hutterite society and have been rare throughout the history of the sect lends support to the sociological structure-function approach in human behavior represented by Robert K. Merton.[90] It seems that in individuals who have acquired a strong superego and are part of a well integrated social system which gives them considerable economic, psychic, affectionate, and social support, psychological problems can exist without being expressed through antisocial acts. The Hutterite social structure gives little encouragement to overt antisocial expressions. To the contrary, many culture patterns function to facilitate individual adjustment to pressures for changes or assimilation without pushing individuals into deviant, non-conformist, or rebellious behavior. These institutional arrangements, which can be designated as *controlled acculturation*, will be discussed in Chapter 12.

If this sociological interpretation has validity, one can predict an increase in the frequency of personality disorders and antisocial activities among Hutterites if their social system breaks down. So far, the group has been fairly effective in holding its membership and in adjusting to social change without individual demoralization. Only the future can tell to what extent the sect can continue to make the present gradualistic adjustments of their 16th century Anabaptist peasant traditions to 20th century urban American values without much individual or social disorganization.

9.

Mental Deficiency

MENTAL deficiency or feeblemindedness implies a lack of normal intellectual development that has existed from birth or was acquired early in life. It is largely a defect in understanding one's environment and in utilizing such knowledge for the purpose of social adjustment and of making a living. The person with mental deficiency is limited in his capacities and total accomplishment in direct proportion to the amount of the defect.[91]

Psychoses and psychoneuroses are disorders of adulthood predominantly and are often functional—that is, without recognized organic pathology. Mental defects begin to show up in childhood; to a far greater extent they involve genetic, constitutional, organic, or injury factors, although authorities cannot agree on the extent to which these contribute to etiology.

Hutterites are quick to recognize severe or moderate forms of mental deficiency. Often the condition is noted by the midwife at birth or shortly after. Mental defect is suspected if a child's physical growth or social maturity proceeds at a noticeably slower pace than that of other children. Hutterites are fairly sensitive to such developmental patterns, because several women in a colony usually have children of the same age and intellectual deviations are easily recognized by comparison. Enumerators could inquire about such cases by asking informants about children unable to attend kindergarten or school. They also could check up on children unable to keep up with their class. However, defectives were less widely known throughout the sect than psychotics. Most defectives are young children, who are less likely to become a topic of conversation than adults. Our staff also did not focus as much attention on the enumeration of mentally defective persons as it did on psychotics.

The differential diagnosis of mental deficiency is commonly based on the degree of social intelligence. In addition, cases are classified, when possible, on the basis of physical symptoms. Among the mental defectives examined by a staff member or medical authority there were four children who were designated by the conventionally correct but scientifically misleading term "mongolian idiot." This number of cases did not appear to be unusual. The mothers of these children were much younger than the mean age of such mothers in the general American population.* There were also two cases of basal ganglion disease, two of Little's disease, two of hydrocephalus, and four of epilepsy. One older woman was a dwarf.

In terms of social intelligence, 15 of the 51 cases were severely defective. They could not talk or walk normally. Usually they could not feed themselves, and some were completely incontinent. None could attend school. Their life expectancy was very short; none of the severe cases were over 30 years of age, and 11 were less than 15. They could

---

* All Hutterite mongoloid children were under 10 years of age. Their mothers had an average age of 29 years at delivery, with none being over 33. The mean age of such mothers in the general population is 41. The prevalence in the general population is about two cases per 1,000 births. The four Hutterite cases occurred in approximately 3,000 births between 1940 and 1950.[92]

all qualify for admission to an institution for permanent custodial care.

Twenty persons were moderately defective. They could
dress themselves, were continent, and could do simple work
under supervision. They normally ate with older persons of
their age in the communal dining room. Only four were over
30 years of age. Many of those who lived to an adult age were
not baptized because they could not memorize the catechism,
but they generally attended church regularly with all the
other people in the colony. None of the patients were married. They could all qualify for admission to an institution
for mental defectives.

Sixteen of the patients were diagnosed as mildly defective.
They generally had some schooling and knew the rudiments
of reading and writing. They participated in the work of
their colony and as adults had a regular work assignment
which required little initiative or skill. Seven of the cases
were over 30 years of age.

About 63 per cent of the Hutterite cases were male. The
preponderance of males was highest for the mild defectives
(11 to 5), less for moderate cases (13 to 7), and almost nil
among those categorized as severe (8 to 7). In view of the
small number of cases in each category, these differences were
not statistically significant, except the over-all sex difference.
A. F. Tredgold,[93] an international authority on mental defects, also noted a preponderance of males in the studies reviewed by him. This statistical sex linkage warrants more
careful study.

Hutterites ascribe some cases of psychoses and psychoneuroses to "bad blood," but this genetic theory is advanced
quite generally to explain the prevalence of 51 cases of mental
deficiency. It will be recalled that Hutterites believe members should marry persons within the sect. The actual choice
of marriage partners is even more restricted, because it is usually made from within the same kinship group. These prac-

tices persist despite the Hutterites' belief that they have deleterious genetic consequences. But factors of faith outweigh considerations of inheritance. Hutterites express mild disapproval of marriages of first and second cousins, but the colonies do not prohibit such unions, which are probably more common in this group than in the general American population. Marriages of mentally defective persons are discouraged. Hutterites generally exercise close protective control over these people. There is no sexual exploitation of defective women. However, the religious value attached to marriage and to having children sometimes outweighs these eugenic considerations. None of the defective adult women could find a husband, but four men were married and had families. They had a total of 22 children in 1951, two of whom were moderately defective. The birth of a defective child in a family is not considered a justification for birth control measures; the family continues to procreate.

The inclusion of mental defects in our study first of all was necessary to distinguish between these severe developmental limitations and those that might appear to be similar but are due to psychoses. Our data also lends itself to the examination of the three important questions:

1. How does the Hutterite frequency of mental deficiency compare to that of other groups? Is there evidence to support the widely held assumption that inbreeding in a population necessarily leads to deterioration in the germ plasm of a population, which shows up in a high frequency of mental deficiency?

2. Do psychoses and mental deficiency occur in a constant ratio to each other in a given population?

3. How do sociological factors affect the manifestations of mental deficiency, even if its etiology is related primarily to genetic, constitutional, organic, and injury factors?

Cross-Cultural Comparison

A comparison of lifetime morbidity rates per 1,000 population of the Hutterite and the nine other populations where census studies of mental disorders were made, does not support the Hutterite beliefs about a genetic "taint." The sect's morbidity rate of 6.0 cases per 1,000 population is not unusual and is the approximate median of the ten rates. (See Table 18.) The Hutterite frequency of mental defects also seems moderate when compared with the results of surveys made in England. The first, made by a Royal Commission in 1904, found a rate of 4.6 cases per 1,000 in a population of close to four million persons. Rural areas had higher rates than urban centers. A similar but more comprehensive study made in 1927, covering a population of 622,880, revealed a rate of defectives of about 8 per 1,000. In rural areas the lifetime morbidity rate was 10.4; in urban areas it was 6.7 per 1,000. In comparison, the enumerated lifetime morbidity rate of the Hutterites certainly is not high.

If it were possible to correct the various rates for differences in age distribution of the populations, the Hutterite rate would rank lower. Mental deficiency is most common among children, who are more numerous in this sect than in any other population. It may be recalled that slightly more than half of the Hutterite membership in 1950 was under 15 years of age. While no precise conclusion is possible about the relative frequency of the Hutterite mental defectives, it is probably lower than that of many populations in which there has been no in-group marriage policy.

We doubt that many, if any, Hutterite cases of moderate and severe mental deficiency were missed. Their symptoms and limitations are so extreme and well known among the Hutterites that they could not easily have escaped the attention of our field staff. There is a strong presumption, however, that our staff failed to enumerate many mild cases. In the 19 colonies surveyed most intensively, the rate was 7.2 per 1,000 population, or 20 per cent greater than in the entire group. In the nine colonies not visited by any staff member, where the enumeration of cases had to rely entirely on Hutterite informants and medical or hospital records, the rate was only 4.0 cases per 1,000. These frequency variations were associated directly with the intensity of the enumeration process, but the differences in the rates were not statistically significant $(P = .71)$.

This clue to incompleteness of enumeration of milder cases is reinforced by the analysis of the paper-pencil rating sheets. It will be recalled that they were filled out by Hutterite and

Table 18—Lifetime Morbidity Rates of Mental Deficiency in Ten Population Studies

Population and Type of Diagnostic Category	Number of Enumerated Cases	Lifetime Morbidity Rate per 1,000 Population
Arctic Norwegian Village		
Oligophrenia	60	45.3
Bavarian Villages		
Poor mentality	4	1.2
Debility	36	11.2
Imbecility and idiocy	10	3.1
Total	50	15.5
North Swedish Area		
Oligophrenia*	99	10.3
Williamson County, Tennessee		
Mental deficiency	203	8.2
Eastern Health District Baltimore		
Mental deficiency	375	6.8
Ethnic Hutterites		
Mental deficiency	51	6.0
West Swedish Island		
Oligophrenia	50	5.7
Thuringia Villages		
Imbecility and idiocy	201	5.4
Island of Bornholm		
Oligophrenia	191	4.2
Formosa Area		
Mental deficiency	68	3.4

* In this study the concept of *oligophrenia* was restricted to ". . . those individuals who are unable to attend ordinary schools, even if instructions are given in special classes. This would mean a dividing line at roughly an I.Q. of 60-70."[94] Mild cases of mental deficiency were therefore not included in the enumeration of cases. It is probable that many milder cases were missed also in all of the other studies.

public school teachers for all school children in 36 colonies. The public school teachers rated 43 children, or 10.4 per cent of those tested, as being quite "dull"; 16 children, or 5.2 per cent, were so designated by the Hutterite religious teachers. Unfortunately, these results did not become available until the completion of our field work. We were therefore unable to determine how many of these "dull" youngsters should have been enumerated as mild mental defectives. We suspect that some would have qualified for this diagnosis, with a resultant increase in the total number of cases.

The strongest evidence in support of the assumption that cases of mild mental deficiency were underenumerated is found in the fact that severe and moderate defectives constituted almost 70 per cent of all Hutterite cases—a very high proportion. In the English studies, the Arctic Norwegian Village, and the Eastern Health District areas, for which there is somewhat comparable information, only about 25 per cent of the cases were in these categories of moderate or severe mental deficiency.

This probable underenumeration of mild cases was conditioned to some extent by the fact that our study was focused on psychoses primarily; other mental disorders were not surveyed with the same degree of intensity or attention. However, probably there also are important cultural factors that contribute to the low frequency of persons recognized by Hutterites as being clearly mentally defective. Within the shelter of their communal economy, a mildly defective individual can function without becoming a community "problem." The sect gives excellent personal attention to defectives, and none have ever been institutionalized. Hutterites consider it a religious obligation to do everything possible to keep them well. Their life expectancy may be greater than that of similar American cases, who are born into families and communities less able or willing to care for them. This factor could account for some of the high proportion of moderate and severe mental defectives enumerated in the Hutterite study.

Mental Defects and Psychoses

According to A. F. Tredgold there is evidence pointing to a fairly constant relationship between the prevalence of mental defects and psychoses. He did not cite the evidence, but pointed out that in England, in 1926, the ratio of known mental defective to psychotic patients was 2.27, more than twice as many defectives as psychotics.[95] The hypothesis that there should be a constant relationship between the prevalence of psychoses and that of mental defects in a population would be tenable only if we could assume that both conditions have a similar etiology. We see no theoretical basis for such an assumption.*

There certainly was no uniformity in this ratio in the ten population studies reviewed in this book. The ratio ranged all the way from 0.34 on the Island of Bornholm to 2.38 in the Bavarian Villages.† The ratio of *enumerated* frequencies of the two categories of mental disorders is not necessarily a good index of what the ratio of *true* frequencies would be if they could be determined. In many studies the efforts made in enumerating mental disorders were not of similar effectiveness for the two categories. No consistent pattern of relationship can be observed between the survey methods em-

---

* Dr. Tredgold's convictions in this matter were changing. His untimely death in September 1952 may have prevented him from making an appropriate modification in his textbook. His son, R. F. Tredgold, of the University College Hospital, London, to whom this section was submitted for comment, wrote: "My father's views on this were based, I think, on his original hypothesis of a neuropathic diathesis. I believe that he was going to modify his ideas on this subject and probably would accept your criticism."

† Other ratios were: West Swedish Island, 0.53; Baltimore Eastern Health District, 0.74; Formosa Area, 0.89; North Swedish Area, 0.93; Hutterites, 0.96; Thuringia Villages, 1.00; Williamson County, Tenneseee, 1.30; and Arctic Norwegian Village, 1.58.

ployed in different studies and the respective frequencies of psychoses and mental defects.

Culture and the Meaning of Mental Deficiency

There is considerable social acceptance of mentally defective persons among the Hutterites. Once a child's retardation is recognized, he is usually taken to a doctor to determine if there is any medical remedy for the condition. If there is none, the child and his limitations are accepted fatalistically. The community provides the family with additional help, if needed, to give optimum physical care to the youngster. In some families the mother will turn the child over to a sister or her mother, who may have more time and patience. Feelings of rejection by the parents exist, but they are usually well repressed. Other children are punished if they ridicule or take advantage of the afflicted child. Defectives who reach adult life are encouraged to work.

Defectives are not thought to be morally responsible for what they do. Those who engage in antisocial activities are punished only if they show sufficient insight to be affected by punishment. The community keeps them in line by watching them carefully. In two cases where mildly defective individuals violated a number of religious rules, the community "cancelled their baptism" rather than excommunicate them. By cancellation of their baptism they were reduced to the status of children, who are thought to be incapable of sinning and therefore can attain salvation automatically.

Some non-Hutterite informants, whose acquaintance with the sect was usually superficial, report impressions that intellectual dullness is widespread. Their judgments seem to be greatly influenced by the fact that Hutterites take little public interest in politics or general education. They do not approve of radios. Film stars, comic strip heroes, and sports celebrities are unknown to most Hutterites, and few read more than their scriptures and the Bible. Many speak a somewhat faulty (but fluent) English. As one of our informants put it: "They are ignorant of the folksy things any American fool would know." Nevertheless, our staff, and most of our professional informants, such as English teachers in Hutterite colonies, doubt that there is anything substandard about the general Hutterite intelligence level. All but a few colonies have excellent leaders who handle business affairs involving tens of thousands of dollars. They buy, operate, and repair complicated machinery. They show considerable intelligence in handling their own community problems. Without such talents, the Hutterite people, who are often an unpopular minority, could not survive, grow, and prosper.

10.

Epilepsy

THE term *epilepsy* is difficult to define. The word is Greek for "seizure." It is a ". . . temporary loss of consciousness without apparent cause; and it is usually accompanied by muscular movements which may range anywhere from a slight twitching of the eyelids to a violent shaking of the entire body."[96] Epilepsy is a category covering symptoms of different disorders affecting the central nervous system and brain. Changes of consciousness without convulsions also occur. Some epileptics suffer from spells of amnesia and perform all sorts of unusual acts. They may run, fight, and scream without being aware of it. Epilepsy is accompanied by changes in the electrical potential of the brain.[97] They can be recognized with the help of a very sensitive electronic apparatus, electroencephalograph, which records the changes of the electrical current produced by the brain. Epilepsy can be caused by gross brain damage due to tumors, injury, and toxic substances like alcohol and uremia. There are also the epilepsies without apparent causes which are commonly referred to as idiopathic.

The classification of the convulsive disorders with mental

disorders is largely a consequence of tradition. Historically, epileptics have often been hospitalized with persons who are psychotic or mentally defective, although most persons with epileptic seizures are mentally and emotionally normal. Traditions are slow to change! Epileptics were enumerated in this investigation because the category is included in the reports of most population surveys of mental disorders. Hutterite informants generally were quick to call attention to such patients. In the sect there were 20 intellectually normal persons who had at some time showed symptoms of epilepsy. Four others, with a primary diagnosis of mental deficiency, could also be included in this category. The total number of enumerated cases was therefore 24, a crude lifetime morbidity rate of 2.8 cases per 1,000 population. It is high in comparison with those enumerated in five other population surveys. (See Table 19.). However, the European studies of epilepsy con-

Table 19—Lifetime Morbidity Rate of Epilepsy in Six Population Studies

Population	Number of Cases Enumerated	Lifetime Morbidity Rate per 1,000 Persons
Ethnic Hutterites	24	2.8
Eastern Health District, Baltimore	126	2.3
Formosa Area	26	1.3
Island of Bornholm	47	1.0
Thuringia Villages	26	0.7
West Swedish Island	2	0.2

centrated largely on the enumeration of epileptics with psychotic disturbances. They either ignored or had little access to those cases who were socially well adjusted. In several of the countries, moreover, there are legal barriers against the marriage of epileptics. Individuals close to affected persons, therefore, had strong motives to be uncooperative with anyone seeking to locate milder or recovered cases.

Benjamin Malzberg, in a review of incidence and prevalence studies, concluded that ". . . approximately 6 to 7 per 1,000 of the population are epileptic." Selective Service statistics for World Wars I and II and a survey made in 1916 in Nassau County, New York, by the National Committee for Mental Hygiene were important bench marks for making this estimate.[98]

By comparison, the Hutterite frequency of cases is low. There is a widespread but as yet unsubstantiated assumption that genetic factors loom large in the etiology of most forms of epilepsy. The moderate frequency of convulsive symptoms in the Hutterite sect raises doubt that the in-group marriage pattern of the group has been a serious threat to its health.

In the Hutterite study inquiries generally did not go beyond an effort to establish the presence of convulsive symptoms and to determine whether the cases had other psychiatrically significant symptoms. We were not interested in studying epilepsy as such, but checked cases for the possibility that they might show a true mental disorder. Despite this limit to our interest, it is doubtful that many cases of epilepsy were missed. Like psychoses, this condition is easily recognized. Hutterites call epilepsy the *Hinfaellige Krankheit* (Falling Sickness) and consider it to be a physical illness; they do not regard it as a possession of evil spirits or the devil, a belief common among Christians in the Middle Ages. As was previously noted, the enumerated rates were highest in the colonies not visited by any staff member (0.53 cases per 1,000), lower in those surveyed briefly (0.21), and lowest in those studied intensively by our staff (0.12). These differences were not statistically significant (P = .46).

All but two of the cases seemed to be of the grand mal variety. There were more than twice as many male as female cases, a ratio of 17 to 7. In 70 per cent of the Hutterite cases the onset of the disorder was noted as occurring before the age of 15. The age and sex distribution was similar to that of epileptic persons enumerated in the Baltimore Eastern Health District. Active symptoms of epilepsy were a barrier to marriage, but six of the patients were married and had children.

In all but one of these persons the symptoms began to appear after marriage. Although Hutterites believe the condition to be hereditary, individuals with convulsive disorders are not encouraged to practice birth control. They go on having children. Healthy siblings of epileptics do not seem to be handicapped in their chances for marriage.

We doubt that more than one or two of the nondefective cases would require hospitalization if they had to live outside of a Hutterite community, although our field work procedures did not permit us to learn enough about the history of every case to make these hospitalization estimates with a high degree of confidence. Only two of the patients had been cured by the summer of 1951, and two others were rated as improved. Hutterites know that epilepsy can be treated through the administration of drugs, and their patients generally are receiving the medications presently found most effective. One woman was "miraculously" cured after falling off a wagon and hitting her head, but the people prefer more conventional methods of treatment. Often Hutterites will travel thousands of miles to one of the nation's outstanding treatment centers for diagnosis of this condition.

In the American society epileptics have difficulty living normally within the limits of their occasional seizures. If their condition is known they are often ostracized. In the Hutterite culture this physical handicap is not compounded with such social handicaps; epileptics are accepted and well integrated socially.

11.

Hutterite "Psychiatry"

PEOPLE with mental problems do not normally take them to psychiatrists, psychologists, social workers, or other trained counsellors.[99] Some of these professionally unattended cases find help in more or less spontaneous social processes of their family, their friendships, and their community. The importance of this informal, lay therapeutic support is well demonstrated by the Hutterites. The sect affords an opportunity to view in a contemporary setting some of the psychological helping processes which can exist in a closely knit community and which may have been common in much of Western Europe prior to the Industrial Age.

Hutterites have a traditional respect for physical medicine. In their early history they encouraged some of their members to specialize in the craft of healing and blood-letting. Their chronicles report with pride that in 1581 George Zobel, one of their physicians, was called to treat Kaiser Rudolph of Bohemia. Contemporary Hutterites, however, object to training their own members in modern medicine. They believe that such "worldly education" would destroy the religious faith of the person receiving it.* There were several self-made but experienced midwives, chiropractors, dentists, and experts in medicinal herbs in the group in 1951. But in most illnesses, particularly those of an organic nature, Hutterites consulted properly trained and accredited doctors.

Symptoms of functional mental disorder were often interpreted first, by Hutterite patients or their family, as organic in origin, as the result of "working too hard," "headaches that won't let a person sleep," loss of appetite, and vague pains in various body regions. A general practitioner was usually consulted. Some of the doctors had little psychiatric sophistication and would make an organic diagnosis. After x-ray and laboratory investigations they would prescribe vitamins or make exploratory operations. Nevertheless, the first clear recognition that the problem had a mental basis often came from a doctor, but Hutterites often tried to get help from several general practitioners before sending a patient to a large diagnostic center, sometimes more than a thousand miles away from his colony.

If a stay of several days or weeks was necessary to be properly diagnosed or to receive treatment, the patient, in the company of a close relative, would reside in a hotel or boardinghouse, if at all possible, rather than in the hospital itself. Once they accepted it as a necessity, Hutterites were willing to get and pay for good medical care.† For example, the

---

* The decline of the tradition of having their own trained medical men is a consequence of repeated experience that a man's Hutterite affiliation is not likely to survive exposure to advanced scientific training. As early as about 1790, the official Hutterite historian wrote: "In a few years three members left our faith. They were among the most skilled and learned among us." One of these deserters was young Christian Wurz, age 26, whom the colony sent to the court of their Russian benefactor, Count Romanzow, to serve as apprentice of the Count's French Physician. Christian Wurz had been selected because of his intelligence and strong faith. He also had a wife and three children in the colony. "But in time," the historian reports, "he began to love the world." He deserted his family and moved to Moscow, "to live in lust and frivolity."[100]

† The average cost of medical, dental, and hospital care and pharma-

writers recently received a letter from the religious teacher of a colony in western Alberta where a young boy is suffering from traumatic epilepsy. He asked: "What do you know about Dr. X—— of Montreal who does epilepsy operations?" Somehow these rural people had heard about this man, one of the world's best neurosurgeons. They wanted to check on his reputation before sending the boy across Canada to be treated by him.

Among the 39 persons having access to an institution with a psychiatric department, 10 were diagnosed as psychotic, 16 as neurotic, 7 as mentally defective, and 6 as epileptic. Four of the psychotic patients were given several shock treatments, as were two neurotics with hysterical symptoms. None of the psychotic patients so treated have recovered completely, although the neurotic patients were relieved symptomatically. No Hutterite was in a mental hospital or an institution for the custodial care of epileptics or mental defectives at the time when our study was completed. None were given any psychotherapy or psychiatric casework.

Cultural Factors in Psychiatric Treatment

The Hutterites' lack of experience with psychiatric treatment is probably not very different from that of other rural and lower-class segments of the population. August B. Hollingshead and Fritz C. Redlich have recently reported that psychotherapy as a method of treatment was largely restricted to patients of the upper sociocultural strata, even in an urban locality where psychiatric facilities were readily available. With few exceptions, lower-class patients received only custodial care or were given organic treatment.[101]

----

ceutical supplies was reported to be about $24 per capita in 1950. We do not have separate statistics on funds spent by Hutterites for the care of their mental patients. There is no doubt that the readiness of each community to assume full financial responsibility for these cases saves many tens of thousands of dollars annually to the State and Provincial authorities where Hutterites reside.

These differentials in access to psychiatric care are probably related to the high cost of modern psychiatric services, particularly of psychotherapy. But there are also important cultural prerequisites for the use and acceptance of these medical skills. The Hutterites' failure to consult psychiatrists as freely as surgeons or general practitioners is a function of cultural barriers.

In psychiatry, even more than in medicine, the doctor must be well acquainted with the patient's entire way of life. Psychiatrists who have treated Hutterites were generally unable to establish proper psychological rapport with them. Most of the doctors were a product of a middle-class North-American milieu and they had difficulty in translating their therapeutic skill into so different a culture. Their preference for treating Hutterites through drugs and shock may have been a form of subconscious rejection of these patients as individuals. It would seem that knowledge of sociological and social anthropological principles are essential for psychiatrists and other clinicians who wish to help those outside their own narrow subculture or class.

The Hutterite culture reinforces these barriers in the doctor-patient relationship. Hutterites tend to regard doctors as *doers*; they expect the physician to make an examination, give an injection, prescribe a drug, or perform a surgical operation. Doctors are readily accepted in the role of active technicians, but they are not trusted in matters affecting the soul or conscience. A psychotherapist who "just talks," and talks about a man's inner life, would be taking over a preacher's prerogatives without a preacher's charismatic qualifications. The Hutterite acceptance of modern medicine, therefore, does not apply to the same extent to psychiatry, psychology, or social case work. In matters affecting the mind and the spirit, Hutterites in 1951 were uncertain as to who can give more effective care to mental patients. They were willing to see what doctors and hospitals could do, but they also had considerable confidence in their own methods of helping.

Hutterite Treatment Methods

The Hutterite outlook on mental disorders is generally optimistic. Hopes for recovery are not abandoned easily. People may be puzzled and awed by the symptoms, but they are not immobilized into fatalistic acceptance of the conditions. In some cases, particularly those diagnosed as mental defects, organic psychoses, and schizophrenia, hope for cure may be given up, as with any chronic disease. But in general Hutterites assume that most mental disorders are treatable, despite their tendency to view the symptoms as resulting from "sin," "the blood," or "nerves all broken up." The hope of curability is reinforced by the fact that those with functional psychoses and neuroses often do recover. The organic and genetic notions about etiology which are prevalent in the thinking of most of these people are counterbalanced by a faith in an all-powerful God. Those with enough faith are believed to be capable of overcoming their "weaknesses"; they are thought to be victims of the "devil's temptations."

The Hutterite attitude towards mental patients is also dependent on the nature of the symptoms. There is compassion for the depressed, defective, or epileptic. There is much identification with those who do not threaten anyone, except perhaps themselves, and who do not violate important mores. In contrast, a handful of psychotic patients and those with character disorder were first regarded as "bad" rather than sick. They used "vile language," were aggressive, resisted discipline, and had delusions in which others were accused falsely. They were excommunicated before their condition was recognized as an illness. Failure to respond to such punishment by introspection and penitence was usually an indication to the community that the person was ill. Once this fact was recognized, patients were accepted by most people with considerable tolerance. They were treated like a child who "did not know any better."

In general, the attitude of most Hutterites towards mental patients differs in two major respects from that common in the general American population:

1. The Hutterite patient, unlike the average American patient, is not socially isolated. The family of the latter generally cannot care for him for financial and social reasons. Often they are ashamed of him. He may be sent away to a mental hospital, more for the sake of the family's peace of mind than for his welfare. The community reaction among the Hutterites is generally more accepting. The patient becomes a center of attention. The immediate family makes arrangements to guard and nurse him at all times; the colony gives whatever support is needed.

2. A psychotic condition does not stigmatize a patient for life. Persons with epileptic fits are not barred from work that they can physically handle, particularly if the seizures are under control. Individuals who recover from a mental disorder can achieve any position in the community. Even while ill they are encouraged to participate as much as they can in the normal life of their group.

Feelings of hostility towards patients no doubt arise among those who are burdened with their care day in and day out. Usually these feelings are not expressed overtly and consciously. Their repression may be made somewhat easier by the recognition given by the community for this work. The Hutterite religion attaches considerable positive value to such a "sacrifice."

The Hutterite technique of handling mental patients varies with the symptoms, but certain generalizations can be made. The methods used may be broadly categorized into six secular and four religious approaches. The former include:

1. FAMILY NURSING CARE

Mental patients live at home, in an environment which is familiar and where they are accepted with some affection. They are encouraged to live as normal a life as they can. Many a psychotic parent continues to look after his children, although usually under close supervision. Sex relations are maintained and most of the married female psychotic patients have had children while they were ill. Special precautions are taken with depressed patients who show suicidal tendencies.

2. PROTECTION FROM SOCIAL-PSYCHOLOGICAL STRESS

Mental patients are kept from situations which seem to disturb them. In one case five sons took turns sleeping in the same bed with their senile father who had great fear of being alone. Colonists did not talk about marriage in the presence of a schizophrenic who reacted with verbal agitation to such conversation.

Psychoneurotic patients are subjected to considerable group pressure to recognize the functional nature of their symptoms. Through humor and admonitions, they are reminded that their symptoms are largely imaginary. But if this approach fails, the colony will in time accept the patient's definition of the situation. Often our staff was told "whatever ails her is in the imagination, but it does no good to tell her so. She's got more pills than a drug store but she should have them, if she thinks they do her any good." The community will allow such persons to see doctors frequently or undergo an operation, even though many recognize the hypochondriac nature of the complaint. In some cases this practice may facilitate the fixation of the neurotic symptoms in a particular region of the body and contribute to making the patient feel more dependent and inadequate.

3. OCCUPATIONAL THERAPY

Psychotic or defective patients are encouraged to work as much as they can at whatever they may be interested in. The emphasis is on trying to get them to mix with people and have normal social relations. Someone the patient likes is assigned to work with him at all times. The patient is not pressed, but is praised for every sign of achievement.

4. CHIROPRACTIC

There are about half a dozen Hutterites who enjoy the reputation of being good chiropractors. They set broken bones, give first-aid treatment, and administer massages for all sorts of vague pains. These people have no special education, although they have read German medical books of pre-World War I vintage. Most of them acquire their "know-how" by watching someone else, usually their father. Several of these chiropractors enjoy an excellent reputation as masseurs among non-Hutterites in the area. Their massages and the personal attention involved seem to give symptomatic relief to many persons with neurasthenic complaints. One Hutterite chiropractor is so much in demand, both in various colonies and in neighboring Canadian villages, that his community has built him a special office and provides a small truck for his emergency calls!

5. VISITING

Vistors in a colony often make a point of calling on psychotic or psychoneurotic patients. This is particularly true of preachers and persons who have had an experience similar to the patient's. They talk to the patient about themselves. People who grew up with the patient but are living in another colony may make a special visit to "cheer him up."

6. TRAVEL

Patients are also taken to make visits. They may travel to a colony where they once lived, to renew old acquaintances. They may be invited to live with a favorite sister or brother for extensive periods, in the hope that the changed environment will do them good. They may also go to town, when someone has to go "on business," more often than they would if they were not ill.

These secular practices have a common psychological element. They single out the patient for special attention. The sick person is accepted as someone who needs opportunities not normally thus available to other members of the colony. Attention as such, regardless of its manifest intent, may have some latent therapeutic effects. It strengthens the patient's conviction that he is important to his family and his community.

This tolerant and supportive attitude has drawbacks for psychoneurotic patients. It facilitates their acceptance of support, protection, and help from their relatives, friends, and physicians in a progressively increasing measure, but often at the price of becoming more dependent upon drugs and other medical treatment. The psychological aspects of their disorder are not often dealt with directly. Nevertheless, chronic malingering is rare. The patient is the final judge of how much he asks (and usually gets) from the group. The knowledge that he himself must set the limits seems to inhibit many psychoneurotic Hutterites from going to extremes. A spinster with many neurasthenic symptoms illustrated this reaction when she explained: "The doctor told me to rest because of my weak nerves, but I helped the girls clean chickens today. There is so much work now." She received praise from her family for the "'sacrifice." She explained later that sometimes she is so busy that she forgets to take the "three different kinds of pills."

These practices are not uniform throughout the culture. Patients receive better care in some families and colonies than in others. The communal concern is likely to be greater for a leader than for a person who has never acquired much prestige. But we know of no case of severe neglect once a person's illness has been recognized. Such recognition may not always come early; some patients do not have perceptive relatives capable of detecting early signs of deviation. However, there are always several people in the community who know the patient well and can to some extent fill this vacuum by providing psychic support.

Hutterite emphasis on religion and personal responsibility is a special source of stress for some members. It tends to arouse deep guilt feelings in those who think that they do not live up to social expectations. But for most members of the society and most mental patients, the religious orientation of their entire way of life also has some therapeutic implications. Four religious methods can be added to the six secular methods itemized above. They are not mutually exclusive and are most frequently used with depressed patients.

7. Prayer

Ministers often go to the home of a severely depressed patient to pray with him in privacy. Church services are held daily in every colony, and patients are encouraged to attend with everyone else. Ministers may lead the congregation in a special prayer for recovery. On occasion they preach sermons designed to fit the needs of a member whom they suspect of requiring psychic support and guidance. Two themes are particularly common:

A. The *forefather* theme. Ministers tell stories about Biblical or early Hutterite inspirational figures who met and overcame problems similar to those of the patient. The implication of such a sermon is: "It's been done before; with enough faith we can do it too."

B. The *divine omnipotence* theme. Ministers never tire of reminding the congregation that Jesus came to save the world and that He will do anything for those who have enough faith.

8. CONFESSION

Religious confession, which has a therapeutic value for some people, is part of the Hutterite religious code. The people believe that all sins must be made known to their preacher. If real or imagined major violations of the mores are involved, such as stealing, adultery, or blasphemy, the elders and to some extent all the adults of a colony must be informed of the transgression. The sinner is punished publicly, either by being chided, by having to stand up in church during the entire religious service, or by being excommunicated for a number of days. However, after he has suffered punishment, "the slate is wiped clean," provided there is true repentance. Guilt feelings can be readily removed under this procedure.

Often the sins about which depressed patients become concerned are minor or imaginary. Preachers have a clearly defined cultural position which enables them to approach such a member. If the preacher in the colony does not feel he has the full confidence of a patient, he can call in a fellow preacher.

9. TOLERANCE FOR DEVIANTS

Despite their orthodoxy, Hutterites show considerable tolerance towards deviants. They believe that all men are born in sin. No person can become a permanent outcast. No one is refused food and shelter. A Hutterite can be excommunicated in a religious sense, but his existence as a human being is never threatened by his own people.

At one time, a member confessed that he became drunk

when on a visit to town and that he may have been seduced
by a prostitute. He was punished by excommunication; less
than a year later, he was elected to a top leadership position.
A one-time thief is now a trusted manager of his colony.
Persons who show peculiar or antisocial behavior can count
on receiving some recognition if they change. It is considered
bad taste to speak publicly about the past transgression of
any member. The group practices follow closely the principles laid down by Andreas Erenpreiss in 1652, in his epistles
on the Hutterite creed:

Christ teaches us therefore to deal with small and petty things
between man and man by means of a brotherly warning and admonition. But if a man is stubborn and does not want to take
brotherly advice, he should be brought before the whole community. If he does not listen to the whole congregation, neither
will he comply nor obey, he should be regarded as a heathen
man and a publican, who has been cut off and excluded. It is
better that the evil member be cut off, than that the whole body,
namely the congregation, becomes confused and spoiled by such
mean people, as we have said in part already above. (Matt. 18.)
Now such warnings and punishments must lead to reformation
and not to damnation. If a member pollutes himself with coarse
and heavy sins and becomes guilty before God, he should be
punished and put to the blush before the whole congregation,
in order to make the matter serious and set an example. Everyone
who is taken into the community promises to accept brotherly
warning and punishment, wherever it may be needed. It amounts
to this: If a member falls into sin, as may easily happen, he
should not abandon his hope and faith, go his way and give up
everything; but he should bear his punishment in tears before
God, recognize his own sin and repent like David, the servant of
God, (Psalm 38, 4-5) or repent in suffering like the prodigal son.
(Luke 15) The saints shall also pray for his forgiveness and the
angels in heaven rejoice over the sinner who repents; following
an honest repentance he will be gladly received back into the
congregation. (Psalm 32; Luke 15.)[102]

10. Culture and Salvation

"Spiritual" therapy goes beyond these well defined practices. In one sense, the entire Hutterite culture is therapeutic. The certainty of its values and objectives can provide guidance to those plagued by psychological doubts, provided they have faith in its basic assumptions. The entire Hutterite way of life is infused with religious significance. There is no clear line separating religious from secular elements. The Hutterite codes are regarded by the sect as ordained by God through Jesus. One need not go to church or pray to achieve spiritual grace. "Good works" for the community, whether milking cows or looking after children, can pave one's road to eternal salvation.

Comparison of Hutterite and Psychiatric Treatment Methods

1. Effectiveness

If effectiveness of psychiatric treatment is measured by the social adjustment of patients, Hutterites do well by their membership. The outlook for recovery of manic-depressive patients is good. Schizophrenics do not often recover, but they learn to live at a socially tolerable level of performance. Mental defectives and epileptics are able to live well within their mental and physical limitations. The environment eases rather than complicates the social consequences of these disorders. The social system is perhaps least therapeutic for psychoneurotic patients. Little is done to help them to acquire an introspective understanding of their functional difficulties. Hutterite mental patients generally learn to function at a socially tolerable level during their illness, despite the partial blind spot of the group for intrapersonal dynamics. But their villages cannot be therapeutic communities for an outsider.

2. SOCIOCULTURAL ORIENTATION

Hutterite "psychiatry" can be helpful only to those who basically accept the value system of this culture. It tries to cure a patient by integrating him more fully in a stable way of life, one which offers a solution to most of the problems of living. The validity of these solutions is reinforced by reference to the Bible, Hutterite traditions and history. Modern psychotherapy is much more relativistic about its values. Each patient is expected to be guided by his own value system, as long as his behavior remains within what is socially acceptable. The patient's own needs rather than those of his group determine the therapeutic goal.

Psychotherapy requires the establishment of rapport between the therapist and the patient. The method of achieving this varies with every situation. Hutterites try to develop communion between the patient and his God. The methods are highly stereotyped; but then Hutterites respond to many of the same cultural symbols. They tend to live up to most of their cultural expectations. They are the product of a fairly consistent socialization process.

Hutterite "psychiatry" emphasizes the importance of the patient's social and value milieu in treatment, with little consideration of the specific and unique psychic problems of the individual. It contrasts sharply with much of modern psychiatry, which is much more psychologically oriented and is focused on the patient. Many contemporary psychiatrists will avoid visiting a patient in his home or meet any member of his family lest such a contact (and new knowledge about the patient) might destroy the transference relationship.* Some

---

* An interesting exception is reported by Maxwell Jones and his associates at the Industrial Neurosis Unit of Belmont Hospital, near London. They found that their experience appears to ". . . justify the conclusion that it is possible to change social attitudes in relatively desocialized patients with severe character disorders, provided they are treated to-

will even refuse to check what contacts social agencies, other psychiatrists, or doctors had with their patient.

It may be stated briefly, with some exaggeration, that Hutterites treat patients by fitting them into a cultural straitjacket. Modern psychotherapy rejects the straitjacket. It treats patients by encouraging them to develop a personal modification of their culture. But no person can go too far in developing such a personal modification. Within more or less rigid limits, all cultures are somewhat of a straitjacket. Also the possibility of development of a personal culture for the patient is limited by the culture's tolerance of deviants. This is perhaps why psychotherapy is more accepted in the United States than in contemporary Europe where it originated.

The emphasis in Hutterite "psychiatry" on social relations, interpersonal communication processes, and basic values of the patient highlights the common neglect of these factors by many psychiatrists. It is probable, however, that much more could be done for Hutterite patients if their problems were viewed in more intrapersonal or psychological terms, without necessarily going to such individualistic extremes as to make the patients misfits in their own society.

3. Future-Orientation

Hutterite "psychiatry" is future-oriented. It does not encourage patients to think about past events in their life or to become deeply introspective. It tries to get them to "wipe off the slate," to think of the future, particularly of religious salvation. This future-orientation clearly contrasts with one of the basic theoretical assumptions in modern psychotherapy: the emphasis on understanding and accepting past events, particularly those of early childhood, and on correlating with infantile experiences current attitudes, behavior, and symptoms.

---

gether in a therapeutic community." See Maxwell Jones, *The Therapeutic Community* (New York: Basic Books, Inc., 1953), p. 156.

4. Emphasis on Repression

Hutterite "psychiatry" depends to a large extent on the reinforcement of suppression and repression. In contrast, modern psychotherapy often seeks to achieve its objectives through encouraging the recall of forgotten memories and events. A psychiatrist might try to get a patient to accept his hatred of his father or his desire to masturbate as "natural." Such an approach would conflict with the Hutterite value system. It could cure a patient only by making him a "bad" Hutterite. Hutterite preachers would advise the member to "forget it." They probably would agree with much of what John Dollard and Neal E. Miller wrote about "Mental Freedom Through Suppression."[103]

Psychotherapy deals particularly with two basic urges, sex and aggression. The overt expression of both these urges is severely restricted in the Hutterite society. Aggression is the object of particularly severe repression. Sexual impulses can be expressed freely within a monogamous marriage, but sexual outlets for unmarried people are taboo. We doubt that these repressive tendencies have pathological effects in this culture. Repression in these areas did not seem to constitute a major problem in most of the persons studied clinically. It would seem that the acting out of both urges can be controlled more easily when the culture and social system reinforce this process.

5. Religious Aspects

The reputation of psychiatry as the most promising of all approaches to the treatment of mental disorders rests, to some extent, on its practical achievements through clinical insights and techniques; but elements of faith are also involved. Modern psychotherapy operates on the basis of promising scientific assumptions, largely untested. As Oberndorf and others have pointed out, there are no accepted standards for measuring the effectiveness of any clinician or psychiatric technique.[104] While the search for testable knowledge is going on,[105] psychiatry is a religion for many patients. Often, against the wishes of the therapist, he is treated by some of his patients like a priest belonging to an "only true church"— a particular school of psychotherapy. A book of that school is regarded as a Bible, and the founder of the school has the final authority of a savior. His offhand hunches may be accepted uncritically as charismatic truths. The confidence of such patients in their psychotherapist has functionally some similarities to the Hutterite faith in a less personal savior. For such patients the role of doctor and "minister" tend to merge. One of the important tasks of the good psychotherapist is to fight this tendency of patients to push him into an omnipotent God or Father role, without at the same time destroying the transference relationship necessary for treatment. One cannot equate modern psychotherapy and faith; there are many elements of science in psychotherapy. But the functional similarities of the psychotherapeutic process in many patients and the relationships of Hutterites to their communities and faith make it seem less strange that the latter appear to give effective aid to many members of the sect who suffer from mental disorders.

Religion and Therapy

In has been shown that religion, which has been the focal point of unity and continuity throughout the four centuries of Hutterite history, can be a major source of psychological support. The social history of similar communal societies, such as the Amana Colonies in Iowa, lends further strength to this hypothesis.[106] Hutterites are kept in line, and by and large are happy to be kept in line, by two main theological sanctions. The first is their belief that all good Hutterites will go to heaven. This is an assured reward for those who live up to their creed. Death is not regarded as an end or a void; for those who walk the narrow path of Hutterite customs it is an opportunity for reunion with departed loved ones. The second is the corollary belief that those who sin will go to hell and eternal damnation. Hutterites believe they are a "chosen people" in the sense that they have a God-given mission to demonstrate by their example the only "true Christian way of life." This belief may be a further source of psychic support. Such self-assurance is particularly important for a minority group that has nearly always been persecuted and is often looked down upon by others as "inferior" and "peculiar."

The high degree of agreement in basic beliefs among adult Hutterites, regardless of colony or generation, is no accident. It is the product of much conscious planning by those who founded the sect centuries ago and those who now give it leadership. There is a well organized system of indoctrination, which has been maintained for centuries to guide the education of children. The consistency of Hutterite values is also facilitated by the sect's general orientation towards the past. Ideas and prescriptions of the Bible, and their written and oral interpretations by men long dead, are regarded as being better, wiser, and morally worthier than anything the present generation might think of. This attitude gives contemporary Hutterites a common focus for orientation. The communal way of living, with the consequent uniformities in dress, housing, food, and other aspects of living, also helps to maintain homogeneity.

Despite this uniformity in faith and in the externals of living, Hutterites are not stereotyped personalities. Differences in genetic predisposition, organic growth, and psychological development seem to be sufficiently powerful to produce an infinite variety of behavior even in a social order as rigid as this one. It seems that the nightmare of uniformity sketched in George Orwell's *1984* or Aldous Huxley's *Brave*

New World is actually beyond realization.[107] At least our study of Hutterite individuals disclosed no simple standardization of personality structure, despite a high degree of communality in social and cultural patterns.

Hutterite individuals differed widely. They were not cast in the same mold, but if viewed as a group they provided an extreme example of the relative importance of ideology and belief among the many personality dimensions which help to shape infants into adult human beings. The importance of values for mental health is not often denied at the theoretical level, but it is at times ignored by practitioners in the process of therapy. "Religion?" is one of the routine questions asked when a person is admitted to a mental hospital. This item of information is used largely to arrange for appropriate last rites should the person die while in the hospital's jurisdiction. Although formal religious affiliations are not important for personality dynamics, strongly held faiths are. We doubt that the Hutterite religious doctrines provide any psychic support as such, but the consistency and sincerity with which they are held probably does. This view was well stated by Sigmund Freud:

How we who have a little belief envy those who are convinced of the existence of a Supreme Power, for whom the world holds no problems because He Himself has created all its institutions. How comprehensive, exhaustive, and final are the doctrines of the believers compared with the laboured, poor and patchy attempts at explanation which are the best we can produce.[108]

Our study supports the conclusion that religious convictions are likely to be important factors in the manifestation and treatment of mental disorders. If this hypothesis is correct, we should find differences in frequency and character of psychopathological symptoms, more on the basis of religious conviction than on that of formal affiliation. Orthodox Jews or devout Catholics should show different symptoms from those of the same faith who are less orthodox. Such distinctions are likely to be missed in any study which breaks down cases into conventional statistical categories based on formal rather than functional religious identification.

The survival of the 16th century Hutterite peasant culture in the heart of the most 20th century-minded continent is a vivid demonstration of the power of values and beliefs. But this dependence on faith is also a threat to the continued existence of this group as an autonomous sect with its present degree of homogeneity. Hutterite leaders and parents are deeply concerned over the influx of "worldly ways" and their competition with colony ways in the minds of the oncoming generation. One test of the culture-dynamic approach in psychiatry may be provided if and when marked cultural changes are experienced by this group. One would then expect to find parallel changes in the symptomatology and frequency of mental disorders.

Multidimensional Psychiatry

Mental disorders cannot be studied adequately in a doctor's office, a clinic, or a hospital environment. They involve total persons who have a body and psyche which is theirs and theirs alone, but who also function within a matrix of interpersonal relationships and social values which they share with many other persons.[109] There is evidence that effective therapy is possible in some cases when primary attention is given to the social relations and values of the patient. Some social workers have long known this and work on this basis in many agencies. Psychiatrists practicing group therapy and theologians teaching pastoral guidance also make this assumption.

The knowledge that therapy can be given through social and cultural channels does not mean that interpersonal and somatic factors are unimportant. There are many roads to a man's mental health; therapists must be trained to proceed along any of these. The greatest probability of success exists when it is possible to treat a disorder in terms of its manifestations in every dimension. We suspect that the understanding of mental disorders, and to some extent their treatment, would be advanced greatly if social and value factors were emphasized as they deserve, and if they were adequately dealt with in the curriculum of medical schools. The average graduating physician is as ill equipped to deal with the emotional and social problems of his patients as the psychologist or social worker is to deal with the physical problems of his clients.

Home Care and Nonprofessional
Treatment Resources

The Hutterite methods of caring for mental patients cannot be applied wholesale to another social system such as the general American culture, which does not have a similar unified integrated value system. We do not live in small, cohesive communities that give an absolute economic guarantee to every member. The sociological orientation of Hutterite "psychiatry" reflects the culture within which it is practiced, just as modern psychotherapy, with its relativism and its office orientation, is a product of our individualistic culture. But some of the principles and practices of the Hutterites have meaning for the larger American scene. Many of America's mental patients, particularly psychotics, generally are treated on the assumption that care under medical supervision is preferable to home care, even when the former is impersonal, superficial, and sometimes more a matter of form than substance. In evaluating the effectiveness of large but understaffed mental hospitals, the Hutterite record with mental patients should be considered. These simple people, without medical skill or scientific training, and often with little psychological insight, are able to care for their mental patients at home with an impressive degree of satisfaction. Force and restraint are not often required. The supportive resources of the patient, his family, his community, and his value system are fully mobilized. This finding fits in with the observation of Albert Deutsch that in "disturbed" wards of nonrestraint hospitals there was "less tension, less violence, less danger, more hope and more healing spirit than on similar wards where restraints are liberally applied."[110]

The Hutterites are not alone in their home and family care of mental patients. In a few American hospitals and in some European countries, selected patients are boarded with rural families who are willing and able to care for them,[111] although, as S. Mayone Stycos has shown, there is little research sophistication in these programs. We need to know much more than is now known about what patients, what families, and what stages of illness are amenable to home care.[112] It is more than doubtful that any modern country can make such extensive use of family and home care methods as the Hutterites in their small, cohesive kinship colonies.* However, the experience of the sect with the custodial care of its mentally ill members serves to underline the possibilities for treatment inherent in the care of some mental patients outside of hospital and institutional settings. The history of treatment of blind and crippled persons has shown that when the public is willing to finance their rehabilitation outside of institutions, with

---

* In one recent pilot study, directed by Helen Walker of the School of Applied Social Sciences at Western Reserve University, advanced social work students examined the records of a sample of 150 patients aged 60 years and older in non-disturbed wards of a state mental hospital. After consultations with the staff of the hospital, the conclusion was reached that the mental hospital was regarded as the optimum treatment setting for only 45.3 per cent of these patients. About 20.6 per cent could have been served better with simple custodial care; 16.7 per cent could have been sent to a nursing home; 12.7 per cent could have been cared for by their own or a foster family. The remaining 4.7 per cent of the patients were severely physically handicapped and required care in a general hospital for chronically ill patients. See Helen M. Walker, *Evaluation of Special Services to the Mentally Ill in a State Hospital* (Unpublished manuscript, 1954), Table 3.

active lay participation by interested persons, the social consequences of their defects can be greatly ameliorated. We know that prisons are more effective in confirming criminals than in reforming them. It may be profitable to investigate similar questions about mental hospitals and their technique of custodial care and treatment.

Another crucial problem of modern medicine is the shortage of qualified psychiatrists. Their number is insufficient to staff existing facilities, grossly inadequate as these are.* Among the attempts to overcome the shortage are interdisciplinary programs including clinical psychologists, social workers, and sometimes nurses. These nonmedical professional persons participate in the process of treatment. There was no treatment program in our study, but in doing research together we gained some insight into the processes of interdisciplinary teamwork.[113] Our joint thinking may be relevant to hospitals and other treatment centers, which have such multiprofessional teams.

The psychiatrist, by virtue of his medical training, has the ascribed status of being most competent to deal with all mental cases. He is expected to make all policy decisions. While there is no question that psychiatrists are required by law to assume certain responsibilities for the care of mental patients in hospitals, this legal responsibility is not necessarily accompanied by an ability to discharge it. A hospital psychiatrist, with inadequate psychological training and sophistication

* "The Federal Census figures covering 248 public hospitals, 186 of them state-operated, showed that in 1947 these institutions had on their staffs a total of 2,004 physicians (not all of whom were psychiatrists), 161 psychologists and psychometrists, 192 dentists, 3,165 graduate nurses and 659 social workers and field workers. The appalling inadequacy reflected in these figures is revealed by the fact that, to comply with American Psychiatric Association standards, our mental hospitals would have to employ 9,000 psychiatrists, 3,000 neurologists, 3,000 clinical psychologists, 40,000 psychiatric nurses and 3,000 psychiatric workers, not to mention 92,000 trained attendants—more than double the number of attendants, trained and untrained, now on the wards." Albert Deutsch, op. cit., p. 146.

about social factors, may be less effective than a well trained psychologist or social worker who works as his subordinate. Even a well qualified doctor may work under conditions in which administrative responsibilities extend to such a large number of patients that a good nurse, or occasionally an untrained but perceptive attendant, has better opportunities to be helpful to a particular patient.* They can know the patient as a person, not simply as a one-page summary.

Our study adds support to the point of view that mental patients can benefit from their contacts with persons of little or no professional training who are capable of positive feelings for the patient. Without accepting as a virtue the regrettable shortage of professionally trained personnel, some improvement in treatment may be obtainable by using potential nonprofessional resources. Relatives, friends, and occasionally ministers may be in this category. At times, it is true, they may have played a major part in producing stress which led to the patient's mental breakdown. Nevertheless they have a therapeutic potential by virtue of their deep emotional relationship with the patient. They have a "direct line" of communication, which in a professional relationship must first be established before psychotherapeutic treatment can take place. Several mental hospitals have recently begun programs of working with relatives of mental patients, on the theory that they need counsel and can be helpful in the process of treatment if given some professional guidance.†

----

* The importance of ward attendants for optimum effectiveness of a mental hospital is recognized in some settings by a change of title to *Psychiatric Aide*. The Menninger Foundation in 1949 established a training school for such semiprofessional aides to develop a standard program that might be used for the recruiting and training of adequate ward attendants.

† We are indebted to Morris A. Ross for calling our attention to several such group therapy programs conducted by psychiatric social workers, by himself at Cleveland State Hospital, Ohio, and by Marian Henderson and John Tabor at Pontiac State Hospital in Michigan. (See *Mental Hospitals*, April 1952, Vol. 3, No. 4, p. 7.)

Our findings, therefore, question the validity of the a priori assumption made by many psychiatrists, clinical psychologists, and psychiatric social workers that mental problems can be treated best by dealing with a patient as an individual in an office, clinic, or hospital. Such therapists consider it to be bad practice to work with the patient in his natural environment, his home and the community where he works. They believe that if the patient is to be treated, his social group should be kept outside the treatment relationship.

Although these nonprofessional resources have been stressed, they must not be regarded as a substitute for conventional professional approaches through organic, psychological-psychiatric, and social case work methods. We suspect that mental patients can be helped through all of these dimensions. They are closely interrelated. Each offers a pathway to the total personality. If one is involved, all the others are likely to be affected to some extent. Their relative emphasis in the process of treatment should vary with the nature of the disorder, the availability of resources, and the cultural and personal background of the patient.

12.

The Impact of Social Change
on Mental Health

MINORITY groups pay a price for their status. Abram Kardiner and Lionel Ovesey, in their book appropriately entitled *The Mark of Oppression*,[114] have shown how people in one minority group experience severe personality problems as they attempt to adapt themselves to the contradictory social forces of assimilation and rejection. Also, beginning with W. I. Thomas and Florian Znaniecki,[115] sociologists have accumulated evidence that the adjustment of immigrants involves group and value conflicts which, particularly in the second generation, are associated with high rates of juvenile delinquency, crime, divorce, desertion, disease, premature death, and other statistically measurable forms of personal pathology.

The Hutterites are an exception to this generalization. Our study has shown them to be unusual, at least with respect to their effectiveness in maintaining a social system relatively free from individuals who are physically or medically neglected and who engage in severely antisocial acts—against either their own group or the larger American society. While the group exhibits a variety of mental disorders, their existence in 2-1/3 per cent of the population does not invalidate the clinical impression of "good mental health" which Hutterites make on those who visit their colonies. Judged by the criterion of frequency of symptoms of severe mental or social disorder, the vast majority of Hutterites live fairly uncomplicated lives.

Are the Hutterites a "healthy" society? In answering this question it must first be noted that the concept of mental health is not a scientific but a value judgment.[116] The Hutterite social system is quite healthy if it is judged by the frequency of antisocial manifestations. Barring drastic changes, the chances are very good on the basis of past performance that a person born into the Hutterite social system will go through life without becoming dangerous to other people, without committing a crime, and without chronically neglecting major moral rules of the American culture or his own. Hutterites appear somewhat less mentally healthy if judged by their own standards. Two or three per cent of their adults have permanently dissociated themselves from their colony. Others have violated their religious principles. For example, some do not live up to the prohibition against the use of communal property for private purposes. A number of young men have served in the armed forces. By the standards of most of their neighbors, these actions are evidence of positive qualities like "independence," "individualism," and "appreciation of the American way of life." By Hutterite values, these actions are judged to be "bad."

Hutterites do not live in a utopia by any of these standards. Death, disease, and personal unhappiness strike them as they strike all human beings. But the pathological impact of these inevitable aspects of living are impressively moderate. The application of the popular concept "mental health" to characterize the group is justified. This generally favorable mental health picture, which impressed social scientists like Bertha W. Clark in 1922 and Lee Emerson Deets in the early 1930's, has been maintained despite the exposure of the Hutterites in America to strong pressures for social change and for assimilation during more than three-quarters of a century. These pressures, which have grown steadily in intensity, come from two directions.

* First, there is pressure from the outside. The colonies are visited almost daily by such persons as salesmen, government officials, teachers, and doctors. The women, who used to get out of the colonies only when they had to go to a doctor, now often accompany the men. Although most of the colonies enjoy a degree of geographical isolation, the "outside," as the Hutterites call it, has broken down the barriers of isolation which their forefathers hoped to maintain when they left Russia. Few colonies are now more than an hour or two from a good-sized city, such as Winnipeg, Manitoba; Lethbridge, Alberta; Lewistown, Montana; or Sioux Falls, South Dakota.

Second, there also is pressure from the "inside." Hutterites, particularly those in the younger age groups, are internalizing some of the values and expectations of their American neighbors. They want more individual initiative and choice, and they consider things regarded as luxuries by their elders to be necessities. There is no area of living in which concepts of right and wrong are not being influenced by the experiences of life in America.

What is somewhat distinctive about social change in this culture is its gradual nature and the institutionalized techniques that have been developed to deal with pressure for change in an organized fashion. Hutterites tend to accept cul-

---

* The material on this and the following pages is being reprinted with permission of the *American Sociological Review* from Joseph W. Eaton, "Controlled Acculturation: A Survival Technique of the Hutterites," Vol. 17, No. 3 (June 1952), pp. 333-340.

tural innovations before the pressure for them becomes so great as to threaten the basic cohesiveness of the social system. We shall illustrate this process of change (which will be defined later as *controlled acculturation*) primarily by reference to the written rules of the Schmiedenleut Hutterites, one of three cliques of colonies which constitute administrative and social subunits of the larger ethnic group.

These written rules constitute no systematic guide to living, as does the Schulchan Aruch of Orthodox Jews.[117] Most problems of behavior among the Hutterites are dealt with on the basis of ancient traditions, which are transmitted to succeeding generations through example and oral communications. When people are sure of one another, no written laws are needed. Families, friendships, cliques, and other primary groups order their affairs on the basis of mores, supported by common consensus. Rules tend to be written down only when this common consensus starts to break down.*

The Schmiedenleut do not usually repeal a rule. When the pressure for change becomes strong enough among the mem-

---

* A study of cultural changes through an examination of such written rules has several advantages. They are what Durkheim calls, the "visible symbols of social solidarity."[118] The written rules are objective evidence that a change has occurred. They do not vary with the biases of the researcher, but express a deliberate intent on the part of those who wrote them.

New rules, among the Schmiedenleut Hutterites, are usually proposed at an inter-colony meeting of elected lay preachers, and are intended to combat a specific innovation in personal behavior of some members, which some of the preachers regard as a violation of the unwritten mores. The new practice must be more than an isolated deviation of the sort which is controlled effectively through the normal processes of community discipline—punishment of the offender by admonition, standing up in church, and temporary ritual excommunication. Only when a deviation becomes widespread in one or more colonies are the leaders likely to appeal for a formal statement of the unwritten community code.

If such a formal rule is adopted by the preachers, it is read to the governing assembly of male members in every colony. Adoption or rejection is by majority vote of all baptized males. Hutterite leaders have their ears to the ground. Their grass-root consciousness is indicated by the fact that in the entire history of the Schmiedenleut colonies, no formal ruling of the preacher-assembly has ever been voted down.

bers to threaten harmony and unity, the rule ceases to be enforced. In time a new rule will be passed to give formal recognition that a new practice is now authorized. What started as a violation becomes the law. The Hutterites are not fanatic. In this they differ from most groups which have established colonies involving communal ownership of property or unusual religious principles. They do not expel a member for deviating a little from the narrow path of custom. Disagreements, new ideas, and personal idiosyncrasies are not completely repressed, although they are not encouraged. Taking their cue from the dogma that man is born to sin, they do not expect perfection from anyone.

The Principle of Communal Property

The Hutterites have had difficulty in living up to this part of their religious doctrine even before their migration to America. Around 1686 most Hutterite communities, which were then established in Hungary and Transylvania, abandoned the community of goods because of what Horsch believes to have been a widespread decline in their spiritual value cohesion.[119] All but those most deeply attached to the Hutterite religion made a permanent break with the sect during that period of crisis and the many decades of persecution by Jesuit priests which were to follow. In 1770, when the remnants of the sect found refuge in south Russia, they were so few in number that all could "live under one roof and eat at one table."[120] In 1819 the principle of communal ownership was completely abandoned by even this small colony of faithful. Not until 1859-60, less than two decades before the migration of Hutterites to the United States, did a remnant of a few dozen families reestablish an association of families with joint ownership of property.[121]

Evasion of the principle of communal property can be observed today in every colony. There are few young men of this generation who have not "earned a little pocket money

on the side" by trapping animals for bounty or fur, by working for neighbors, and, in rarer cases, by selling for their private gain produce which belongs to the community. Leaders
tend to tolerate these practices if they are not carried on too
openly and to excess. They believe that these violations are a
temporary phase of adolescent protest. By the time the boys
become baptized, marry, and assume some administrative responsibility in the community, they "usually grow out of this
foolishness." Most of them actually do, but some ambivalence
towards the principle of communal ownership of everything
is still present in most adult Hutterites.

Much more vigilance is shown in combating the earning of
private income by adults. There is a rule that money received
for work done outside the colony has to be given to the
elected manager. Efforts at selling colony articles to obtain
money were widespread enough to require blocking by rules,
such as the one in 1933 which declared that: "Taking wool
to make socks or blankets and then selling these for profit
does not belong to our life and shall not be permitted." Five
years later a more detailed regulation also prohibited the selling of feathers, wool, soap, socks, gloves, and specific food-
stuffs. Down feathers were apparently the easiest to sell. Regulations forbidding their private sale appear again in 1941.

American business men at times give presents in cash or
kind to individual Hutterites who have done favors for them
or whose good will they are anxious to secure. Such gifts
create a problem in a community where there is supposed to
be an equitable sharing of all material goods. There is a 1926
regulation which provides that presents of clothing received
by members be subtracted at the time of distribution of clothing by the colony. "Other presents must be looked over by
the preacher and manager, who decide what disposition is to
be made of them." Money received as a present was to be
turned over to the manager according to a 1891 decree, although 25 cents of it could be retained for spending money.

In recent years, colonies have been trying to combat private earning through distributing monthly cash allowances to each member, with which he can purchase food, candy, or other articles not considered taboo. In 1941 the Schmiedenleut colonies adopted a uniform standard for this practice: "All people over 15 years of age shall receive two dollars and forty cents spending money a year. It shall be distributed in monthly portions to the father in each family. It shall be spent only for edibles. Children under fifteen years and over six months shall get five cents per month. For unbaptized children, the allowance shall be given to the parents." In some colonies the allowance has been recently raised. The leaders also purchase for general distribution quantities of fresh and canned fruit, candy, and toys. Formerly these items had to be purchased by each person with his allowance.

Adjustments to the impact of individualistic values are being made, but these controlled concessions to the demand for change also serve to underline that there is still considerable strength in the belief of contemporary Hutterites in the community of goods.

The Principle of Austere Simplicity

The pressure for assimilation is equally strong on the Hutterite principle of austerity in consumption. The sect lives in a country in which the encouragement of fashion and conspicuous consumption is a major concern of a billion-dollar advertising industry. As early as 1883 it was necessary to combat fashion in the form of a rule to forbid "ivory rings or red ribbons on the harnesses of horses." An 1886 rule stated that "four-wheeled baby carriages are not permitted." In 1926 another rule affirmed that "baby cribs shall remain as always, namely simple wagons with a pole," to insure that the Hutterites "keep to the old way."

The Schmiedenleut Hutterites have several regulations designed to keep personal consumption on the basis of need and equality within each level of need. For instance, a family of six or more may have seven chairs; one with four or five may have four; one with three or fewer members may have three chairs.

The zeal for austerity in consumption has limits. It appears that the Hutterites are careful not to be excessively severe in restraining strong drives. They reduce the temptation to violate rules by not forbidding all enjoyment of food, drink, sex, and adornment. Hutterites enjoy eating. They are encouraged to get married. "Simple" decorations and colors in clothing are authorized. Wine, beer, and occasional hard liquor are distributed in moderate quantities. The rules are only directed at what the culture considers excesses. This principle of moderation is well illustrated by a 1925 rule to put an end to what are considered excesses at weddings, when the community provides quantities of alcoholic beverages for the celebration of festivities:

When there is a wedding, nobody shall take the liberty of carrying home drinks or taking away from the wedding that which he could not drink. This because human natures are different. And everyone shall drink only so much that his conscience remains clear, because all excess and misuse are sinful. Only if somebody, because of his need to work, cannot be present when drinks are poured, can he come later to the person charged with pouring and ask for his share. But he must not take it home. If somebody is sick however, and cannot attend the wedding, the manager shall give him his share in all fairness.

The largest number of austerity rules are concerned with clothing. Hutterite clothing is the visible symbol of their autonomy. The forces of assimilation are most easily brought to bear against this form of symbolic segregation. It is external to the person, and its change seems to be just a trivial matter. Among the Hutterites, as in other groups, changes in dress often symbolize the beginning of a major break with the past.*

---

* Pauline V. Young, *The Pilgrims of Russian Town,* Chicago: Uni-

One Hutterite regulation exhorts members to ". . . start no new styles. . . ." But the style urge is strong and one can expect many rules on this subject to be issued to keep up with the genius of younger Hutterites for expressing themselves. Hutterites needed to be reminded in 1909 that they must not make "rolled caps" for children, nor add colored strings or bands. Black hats were the only kind permitted by a 1936 rule, which added that "recently purchased white or grey hats should be worn out this year," indicating that they were contrary to the unwritten tradition. Two years later, another regulation was necessary to include pith helmets in this prohibition, since some Hutterite youngsters had begun to purchase them because "there is nothing in the regulations against them."

Schmiedenleut tradition required the use of hooks and eyes to fasten clothes until 1926, when it was decided that buttons on winter clothes "could be retained." The ex post facto regulation acknowledging this change in fashion also sets clear limits: "Only black buttons could be used, except on white garments, where there should be white buttons." But the tendency to use buttons in colors contrasting with the cloth persisted, and twelve years later the 1926 regulation had to be virtually repeated. Emphasizing that buttons should be of the same color as the garment, the preachers added: "Let

---

versity of Chicago Press, 1932. The author found this to be the tendency among the Molokans, a Russian religious sect with strong community ties, which disintegrated rapidly in urban Los Angeles, where the pressures for assimilation proved to be too strong for the internal forces of cohesion. Her account of the significance of a Molokan girl's struggle with fashion would not have to be changed to apply in full to the Hutterites.

"Once I mustered up courage to buy a hat for one dollar and ninety-eight cents. When my mother heard about the hat, she cried and carried on something terrible. 'A hat, what next!' To avoid trouble, I left my hat at a girl friend's house and called for it every morning, ditching my shawl" (p. 163).

Hutterites experience similar conflicts, but very few girls have "ditched their shawls."

everyone be warned of the dangers of misfortune and eternal damnation."

A strict rule in 1933 demanded that "sweaters . . . be summarily gotten rid of, since they do not belong to our world and only lead to improper dealings. . . . He who does not obey shall have his taken away and burned, and the violator shall be punished." The unusual vehemence with which it is worded may pertain to the fact that sweaters are clinging garments which reveal the human form quite faithfully. Other rules require that dresses be kept within five or six inches, and trousers within three or four inches, of the ground. This vehemence of opposition is not applied to all efforts to substitute factory for home-made products. As early as 1911, a regulation authorized that, "A suit (tailored in colony style) shall be bought for all brothers . . . worth about five to six dollars." And in 1917 fur linings for winter clothes were authorized for purchase. After 1921 some "high shoes" (for Sunday) could be purchased in place of homemade ones. In 1938 mattresses "costing no more than fifteen dollars" could be distributed to families which would then have to forego their quota of feathers, traditionally the material used in homemade mattresses. By 1944 the purchase of all types of shoes was authorized, but only in styles approved by the preacher, the manager, and the shoemaker.

Concessions are being made. When the pressure for change becomes too great, we find here as previously a willingness to change a little. In the long view of history, these changes may accumulate to have major consequences.

The Principle of Self-Sufficiency

Farmers generally tend toward greater self-sufficiency than city dwellers. In frontier days they had no choice but to be self-sufficient. Specialized services were not available to them. Their cash income also was usually too low to pay for haircuts in a barbershop, meals in a restaurant, or canned goods from a store. For Hutterites, the preference for self-sufficiency has always had more than an economic motivation. It functions to keep down the frequency of business contacts between members of the colony and outsiders. It also reflects the religious emphasis on austere simplicity.

The effective system of communication throughout America, with its modern roads, its radio, and its press, as well as the economic pressure for the use of technological improvements, made it impossible for the Hutterites to maintain the degree of isolation that had been possible when they lived among Russian peasants. The group is now adjusting itself to these technological and social forces. Very much unlike the anti-machine-age Amish people, Hutterites have no religious taboos against new inventions as such. Their basic attitude is to be tolerant of the use of technology in production, but to be more insistent upon homemade products in consumer goods.

For a long time Hutterites resisted the use of motor vehicles, which could take members to the "temptations" of towns "too easily." The first formal decision concerning trucks was made in 1928. It called for their complete disposal ". . . in view of the misuse and annoyance associated with them." But the pressures for their use proved to be too great, and two years later, permission was given for each colony to rent trucks up to 25 times a year. The following year the rental limit was extended to 30 times a year, although preachers and unbaptized males under 25 years of age were prohibited from driving. In 1933 the rule was changed to permit the use of trucks without any numerical limit, but "they could not be owned, nor rented for more than half a year and they were not to be kept on colony property." In 1940 came a most significant concession: "Preachers may drive trucks like other brothers."

Passenger cars are still forbidden. They are defined as luxuries. In 1951 two Schmiedenleut colonies which had purchased station wagons were ordered to dispose of these too "up-to-date" vehicles. The importance attached to this decision is underlined by the fact that for the first time the preachers decided to accompany this regulation with a definition of what is a station wagon, copied from the *American College Dictionary!*

The gradual acceptance of factory-made devices is important largely because of the recent acceleration of this trend. Imperceptibly to many Hutterites, their concept of what constitutes luxury is changing. Both barn and kitchen are now equipped with modern refrigeration systems. There is even talk of a dishwashing machine to lighten the burden of the women-folk, to whom a hair ribbon or silk stockings still are tabooed objects. Here is a partial list of "luxury" items found in the home of a prominent leader.

A painted photograph of a son in army uniform.

A set of enamelled grocery cannisters, all empty since no cooking is done at home.

A small night light.

A venetian blind in one of the two living-room windows.

A rayon souvenir pillow.

A cigarette stub in an ashtray. (Hutterites consider smoking to be sinful.)

An electric shaver.

A silk handkerchief from the New York World Fair.

Artificial flowers in a decorative flower pot.

Two pin-buttons pinned on a wall decoration over the bed of the colony's most attractive adolescent girl. The respective texts of these buttons were: "I am thin, but oh my!" and "Oh, baby, you do it so nice!" These were gifts of one of her Hutterite beaus.

The occasional sales representative or idle traveller who visits the colonies will notice little of this. The uniformity of polka-dotted black and white kerchiefs worn by all women, the majestic beards of the married men, and the pastoral scene of ducks and geese in the community courtyard may hide the fact that behind this apparently unchanging façade, old and new values are waging a silent struggle within the heart of every Hutterite.

In all this we must not overlook that relative self-sufficiency remains a potent weapon in the Hutterite battle for cultural cohesion. Among the farm enterprises in most colonies are dairying and the keeping of beef cattle, sheep, swine, chickens, ducks, and occasionally turkeys for the "outside" Thanksgiving market. Nearly all colonies grow their feed, except for protein concentrates. They make their own bread from grain. Butter, honey, potatoes, vegetables, fruits, meat and nearly all the things which come to the dinner table are home products. Most clothes, furniture and bedding are still homemade.

Change by Controlled Acculturation

The Schmiedenleut regulations illustrate the persistent efforts of the Hutterite people to control rates of social change by defining the areas in which it is to be approved. When the pressure for change becomes too strong and the rules are violated widely enough to threaten respect for law and order, the Hutterite leaders push for formal change of the written law before it makes too many lawbreakers. By bending with the wind, Hutterites have kept themselves from breaking. This policy was explained by one of their outstanding leaders as follows:

I belong to the conservative faction that believes in making changes as slowly as possible. We Hutterites certainly have changed radically, even during the last decade. Sometimes I get the feeling we will not survive because we go too much with the world. But my father used to think the same thing when I was young, and we are still going strong. We must progress slowly. We should be conservative, although the Apostle Paul said, "Make use of the things of this world, but do not abuse them." You can make changes as long as you do not sacrifice principle. There is conservatism that is right and one that is foolish. We look for the happy medium.

This process of change might be designated as *controlled acculturation*. It is the process by which one culture accepts a practice from another culture but integrates the new practice into its own existing value system. It does not surrender its autonomy or separate identity, although the change may involve a modification of the degree of autonomy.

Controlled acculturation can be practiced only by a well organized social structure. There must be recognized sources of authority. The presence of this practice is evidence that the culture has considerable vitality for growth and continuity, despite the pressures for change to which it is making an adjustment. In the controlled acculturation of Hutterites, there is rarely any fundamental negation of the group's own value system. When they adopt American ways they do not become personally identified with the mainstream of the American culture. They remain Hutterites, loyal to their autonomous way of life.

The process of controlled acculturation cannot be continued indefinitely without ultimately resulting in more assimilation. The concessions made by the Hutterites to their American environment are affecting not only their practices, but their value system as well. In time, the changes may accumulate to bring about a major shift in values, which could destroy the group's existence as a separate ethnic entity.*

The controlled acculturation of Hutterites has been criti-

---

* This concept of acculturation is similar to that defined by the Social Science Research Council Subcommittee on Acculturation. See: Melville J. Herskovitz, *Acculturation*, New York: J. J. Augustin, 1938: 10-15; Ralph Linton, editor, *Acculturation in Seven Indian Tribes*, New York: D. Appleton-Century Company, 1940: 463-464. The Subcommittee also makes a distinction between acculturation and assimilation. It points out

cized by some of their neighbors. There have been unsuccessful efforts to penalize them for their slow rate of Americanization through special discriminatory legislation in Manitoba, Montana, and South Dakota. In Alberta, pressure groups of self-styled patriots were successful in pushing the Social Credit Party leadership to enact a land law which is offensive to many Canadians who treasure their country's strong traditions of civil and religious liberty. The law[122] singles out Hutterites to prohibit their lease or purchase of land within forty miles of any existing colony. It was hoped that this provision would reduce the group cohesiveness by keeping colonies more isolated from each other. The opposite is taking place. Hutterites are in the process of establishing a formal church structure including all of their colonies,[123] which would make it more difficult for any single community to make major innovations of social practice. Many leaders see in this discriminatory law an act of God to warn "His People." It has strengthened the resolve of many younger Hutterites to be wary of "outsiders who hate us." It functions to increase their in-group orientation.

Controlled Acculturation and Personal Adjustment

The strong communal organization which enables the Hutterites to make a planned retreat in the direction of assimilation, in the form of controlled acculturation, probably contributes to the good adjustment of individuals. Unlike the natives in the Pacific Islands or the Poles of America's ghettos,

that no clear line can be drawn between the two processes. In this discussion we reserve the concept of assimilation to denote the end-product of a process of acculturation, in which an individual has changed so much as to become dissociated from the value system of his group, or in which the entire group disappears as an autonomously functioning social system. Acculturation, on the other hand, is reserved for those changes in practice or beliefs which can be incorporated in the value structure of the society without destruction of its functional autonomy.

Hutterite individuals are not being forced, almost overnight, to make a transition from the security support of their *Gemeinschaft*, with primitive peasant values, to an unfamiliar *Gesellschaft* society with 20th century American values. They make the change slowly enough to enjoy community support in the process.

Many members of American minority groups have become marginal and disorganized when caught in a culture conflict. Immigrants lose confidence in their ancestral culture. Their children tend to reject the old-fashioned practices in which their parents no longer believe, but to which they adhere for lack of alternative. They become what Stonequist calls *marginal men*—people without secure roots or values.[124] The high rates of crime, delinquency, prostitution, and venereal disease, and other indices of social disorganization commonly found in this marginal second generation of immigrant groups, can be viewed as a social price of their rapid assimilation without much in-group support.

No such pronounced tendency of individual demoralization was observed among the Hutterites. Hutterites are generally self-confident about their group membership. There are few signs of self-hatred and the sense of deep personal inferiority commonly found among assimilationist Jews, who feel ambivalent about their relationship to the Jewish group.[125]

The factors responsible for this phenomenon are no doubt numerous and are beyond the scope of this book, but controlled acculturation is one of them. This controlled process of adjustment to social change gives group support to the Hutterite individual who must adjust his way of life within the conflict of his own 16th century Anabaptist peasant traditions and the 20th century American values of his environment. Hutterites are making the adjustment, both as a total culture and as individuals, while maintaining a considerable measure of functional adequacy and self-respect.

Mental Health and Conformity

If the theory of controlled acculturation is valid, those who favor the status quo and conformity in social relationships might be tempted to claim: "Science *proves* that conservatism is healthy for both individuals and the social system." The insistence of some people on the need for major reform, drastic change, and radical innovation would appear to be "dangerous." If individual mental health is accepted as an ultimate end or value, this contention is probably correct when applied to the members of a fairly uniform group like the Hutterites. However, this view would not be valid for persons who regard creativity, inventiveness, and new experiences as ultimate ends or values of human existence. The Hutterites are willing to make use of modern technological inventions, but there is virtually nothing in their culture which would support the inquisitiveness of a Leonardo, an Edison, a Freud, or an Einstein.

Other limitations to the generalization that controlled acculturation contributes to individual adjustment are the small scale and high degree of integration of the Hutterite world. This situation is not comparable to a large-scale and less homogeneous social system, like the American society. There many value standards co-exist. Conformity and status quo, which might be important for the mental health equilibrium of one element in society, can be a severe source of social and psychological stress for others. For example, some men of white skin color believe in the ethical virtue and divinely ordained validity of a racial caste system. They live together with many Negroes and whites who believe otherwise and who accept the ultimate validity of the American equalitarian creed. The status quo might maximize the chances for mental health of those whites who uphold the caste system, but it impairs the adjustment of both whites and Negroes for whom this system and its practices are morally unacceptable. Science cannot provide an answer to the question of whose mental health is more important. Controlled acculturation, urged by those who opposed effective social action in the field of race relations, does not help to maximize the mental health of those who are unwilling to accept a "pie in the sky" promise of a "gradual solution of the race problem in a few generations." They want immediate access to equal opportunities for those who do not now have them and who will not live long enough to see that distant era when "the problem may solve itself."

In a complex and diversified social system there can be no single mental health standard. There may be wide agreement that severe mental disorders are "bad," although in many primitive groups men who have hallucinations are given the high status of medicine men, and in our own American and other contemporary societies men with severe psychoneuroses and character disorders are sometimes elected to positions of leadership. There certainly is far less agreement on positive mental health components. The American Hutterite looks with self-satisfied complacency at his crop, the sunset, and his children who surround him in old age. He feels genuinely sorry for his "poor city neighbor who can't see a sunset because the houses are so tall, who earns his living while sitting behind a desk, and whose children will leave him to make their own way." On the other hand, the non-Hutterite visitor to a colony may wonder how men can be happy without education, music, art, and many of the creature comforts which technology can provide. Science can make some cross-cultural generalizations about severe mental disorders; it can generalize much less about mental health, which is a more normative and a less scientific concept.

The limits of the mental health implications of controlled acculturation in a complex society can be illustrated by calling attention to the fact that the Hutterite society, like all cohesive groups, tends to be therapeutic for conformists but puts the unusually gifted individual under considerable social and psychological pressure. Most Hutterites like their lot. They are free to leave their colony at any time. But the Hutterite socialization process does not prepare members for living on their own on the "outside." The prejudices of many Americans against "strange" people also act as barriers to those Hutterites who might be inclined to strike out on their own. The fact that most people reared in the sect retain their membership even when they are exposed to close contact with a technologically superior way of life leads us to conclude that to a fair degree Hutterites get from their way of life what they want. This is possible because they are carefully brought up to want little more than they can get. This social equilibrium is facilitated by the Hutterite emphasis on tradition rather than on change. Life is basically oriented on the status quo. People are not trained to live creatively with uncertainty, relativity of values, and multiple choice. The boy who dreams of being an airplane pilot becomes an adjusted carpenter because his life in the colony succeeds in convincing him that he had just a "silly boyish notion." Religion plays an important part in this process of sublimation. As one middle-aged man confided to us: "I could not be wild like these pilots and live right. I would not mind flying in a jet plane, but I want to fly to heaven more badly."

For deviants the culture is less healthful. It is an extreme example of orthodoxy. The innovator who rejects a few of his environmental compulsions to achieve a new way of life exists, but he is quite rare. Some of these unusual people become leaders, particularly *bosses* and preachers. In these positions gifted men can find socially acceptable ways for expressing themselves, provided they do not deviate too much from the established order of doing things. Less brilliant deviants, however, are likely to become problems to themselves and the group. And women have few opportunities for giving expression to unusual capacities without becoming maladjusted. There is not much room for doubt about any of the main precepts of the Hutterite value system.

The dilemma of mental health in a less conformist world may be illustrated by the intellectually curious carpenter's daughter in South Dakota. She took correspondence courses after she left school at the age of 15 and five years later earned a high school certificate. Her great-uncle, the manager of the colony, recognizing her ability, asked her to keep the colony books. Through him she became the de facto manager of the colony, a position she could never occupy formally because of her sex. When we first met her, she was considering plans to attend a nearby college to study nursing and to reorganize Hutterite public health practices. She was an outgoing person and a cheerful and creative collaborator in our study. Two years later she refused to give any further aid and asked our staff not to visit her again. She spent much of the day in bed and had many neurasthenic complaints. She had married a young boy, "to be just like the other women." She explained that it was best for her mental health to be more of a conformist: "I had been doing too much reading and writing for my own good."

Science can offer no universally valid criterion for evaluating the "mental health" of this gifted young woman's mode of adjustment to conflicts involving a more complex modern culture. Few Hutterites would question the wisdom of her decision, although the group may have lost a potential Florence Nightingale to gain another housewife and mother. The reader shall have to judge for himself, on the basis of his own values, what he thinks of this purchase of social acceptance at the cost of a neurosis.

Conclusion

THIS book deals with the very broadly stated theory: *Cultural and social variables affect mental disorders.* It is one of a number of recent efforts to explore the relatively neglected social and cultural aspects of mental health and mental disorders. The emergence of interest in this area, in social psychiatry, may represent a significant shift away from the primary, and sometimes almost exclusive, biopsychological emphasis of psychiatry during the first few decades of the 20th century, which in turn had been a reaction against the overemphasis on the genetic and organic aspects of mental disorders during the late 19th century. In recent decades the role of social and cultural factors in psychopathology has rarely been denied in theory. In practice, however, these factors have been least and last in the focus of attention of most psychiatrists, psychologists, social workers, and others professionally concerned with the clinical study and treatment of mental disorders.

This study was conducted in an unusual human laboratory —a society whose members share over four centuries of common history, tradition, and faith, and are bound together by many close kinship ties. They live in modern America, under the impact of its technology and its way of life, but sufficiently apart from it to constitute a miniature autonomous social system. The Hutterites were willing to co-operate in this scientific venture; they did so with a generosity and completeness rare in the annals of social science. Some of the cultural and social variables like educational level, income, migration, and others, which in other populations usually vary greatly, could be eliminated as factors because they vary little throughout the entire society. It has a relatively low level of social stress, in the sense that its way of life lacks many of the unresolved tensions and contradictions of the contemporary American melting pot cultural system. It was also possible in this study to co-ordinate to some extent two research approaches which are frequently mutually exclusive. We were able to obtain a clinical understanding of Hutterite individuals, both the mentally healthy and the mentally ill. At the same time, it was practicable to survey the entire population for patients who had ever been mentally disordered. We could make a statistical census and classify people in a variety of sociological and diagnostic categories, without having to forego close personal contact with an adequate sample of the entire group. In view of the high degree of cultural homogeneity, these clinically observed individuals, although not selected at random, included persons of both sexes and of various ages, occupations, and statuses.

Our findings do not confirm the hypothesis that a simple and relatively uncomplicated way of life provides virtual immunity from mental disorders. From Virgil to Thoreau certain philosophers have had little doubt about the validity of this assumption, and some modern anthropologists and psychiatrists have offered observations which seemed to bear them out. Psychoses and other forms of mental disorder were found to occur with regularity in the Hutterite population. Their existence in so secure and stable a social order suggests that there are genetic, organic, and constitutional elements which predispose a few individuals to mental breakdown in any social system, no matter how protective and well integrated it may be.

Our findings contain no blueprint for a "perfect" social order. On the contrary, a mental health utopia is probably impossible. The strong social cohesion and clear-cut expectations which tend to protect Hutterites from having to face the uncertainties of life unaided and without normative guidance, can also be a source of psychological stress. Strong guilt feelings were found in Hutterites who feared that they might be unable to live up to the expectations of their group. Severe depressive moods were the most common psychopathological symptoms in neurotic and psychotic members of the sect. The emphasis on mutual aid, social security, friendliness, and nonaggression, which impressed the researchers and previous students of Hutterite life, also had negative consequences for social and psychological adjustment, particularly of individuals who were social deviants. It is probably valid to generalize that no cultural trait is inherently positive or negative for mental health. All tend to produce individual behavior which can be regarded as "good" or "bad," depending on the value standards of the people affected.

There is, however, evidence of the existence of cultural differences in the probability of exposure of individuals to experiences and stresses which lead to psychotic, psychoneurotic, or other forms of disturbed behavior. Mental disorders are not randomly distributed throughout the human race. We judge that the Hutterite lifetime risk of all types of mental disorders is as low as or lower than that of any contemporary Euro-American group within the Judaeo-Christian complex of cultures for which comparable data was available, but it is probably higher than the frequency of these disorders on the Island of Formosa. This tentative conclusion is based on our analysis of frequencies of mental disorders in ten populations, although the data available for the comparison are very limited in all categories of mental disorder except psychoses. The Hutterite enumerated lifetime morbidity rate of psychosis ranked third highest among the ten groups, but the true rank order is probably much lower, when allowance was made for known methodological short-comings of the enumeration procedures of the different studies.

The qualitative evidence in support of this conclusion showed much internal consistency. Hutterite mental patients with a variety of functional disorders reflected Hutterite cultural values in their symptoms of illness. There was little free-floating anxiety among the people who had grown up in this highly structured social system. Dominance of depression and introjection rather than acting out or projection of conflicts was found in both manic-depressive reaction and psycho-neurotic cases. Nearly all patients, even the most disturbed schizophrenics, lived up to the strong taboo against overt physical aggression and physical violence. Paranoid, manic, severely antisocial, or extremely regressive symptoms were uncommon. Equally rare or completely absent were severe crimes, marital separation, and other forms of social disorgan-ization. People had interpersonal problems rather than anti-social manifestations. Hutterites showed evidence of having aggressive impulses in projective tests, but these impulses were not manifested overtly as acts physically harmful to others. Human brutality may be found in most social sys-tems, but it is not a functionally necessary behavior; its re-pression seems to be possible.

The traumatic social consequences of mental disorders for the individual patient, his family, and his community were ameliorated by many Hutterite practices. The onset of a symptom of disorder served as a signal for the entire com-munity to demonstrate support and love for the patient. He was generally approached with considerable sympathy and understanding. Mentally ill persons were treated as "ill" rather than "crazy." All but one case could be looked after in the home, usually by members of the immediate family. Patients were encouraged to participate in the normal activities of their family and community, and most of them were able to do some useful work. Rarely were their afflictions regarded as a social disgrace. No permanent stigma was attached to those who recovered. Symptoms of disorder were relatively bearable for the patient, his family, and his community. There seemed to be little need for the severely restrictive care which is so characteristic of many mental hospitals. This fact supports the theory that many of the severe disturbances of some psychoses and personality disorders are not an inherent attribute of these conditions. At least in part they seem to be a consequence of the methods of handling patients used by hospitals, families, and communities.

The Hutterite way of life was no antidote for severe mental disorders, but it provided an atmosphere within which emotionally disturbed persons were encouraged to get well or to function in a socially accepted manner within the limits imposed by their illness. While the prospects for recovery for Hutterites suffering from a manic-depressive psychosis were no higher than those of other American mental hospital patients in the same category, Hutterite colonies were therapeutic communities in the sense that the traumatic social consequences of being mentally ill were kept at a minimum.

The cost of medical care was not a source of individual concern, for the community paid all medical bills and provided patients with a guarantee against a lower standard of living during illness. Nor did illness create an overwhelming burden for those who were required to nurse a patient; the community provided them with additional help. Children of sick parents were not neglected. Members recognized this provision for medical insurance as an important benefit. Their "group health insurance scheme" did not result in excessive costs or widespread malingering. Factors other than economic governed the use or abuse of such free facilities. In this small, cohesive primary group, social pressures were brought to bear on those who abused the system. Some Hutterites were inclined to pamper themselves medically, but they were ashamed to follow these inclinations without "adequate" (socially recognized) cause. The Hutterite religion indoctrinates most members with a deep responsibility towards their society. Work is positively valued. It was observed that Hutterites actually took less advantage of the facilities of modern medicine than is desirable by the best medical standards. But their failure to consult doctors early, often, and regularly enough was not caused by economic limitations; it was largely a reflection of insufficient knowledge of and confidence in some branches of medicine.

Our study was concentrated on the 2-1/3 per cent of the population who were or had been mentally ill at some time, but it was not restricted to this group. The presence of significant positive mental health elements can be inferred from the fact that more than 97 of every 100 Hutterites living in 1950 had not experienced a major mental disorder. Most members of the sect showed a high level of personal adjustment to the conditions imposed by their state of physical health, psychological needs, and way of life. They were able to meet the usual life demands inherent in love, hate, work, child-rearing, sickness, and death. Most Hutterites were satisfied to live within what they call the "narrow path" of their culture. The sect succeeded in shaping the great majority of Hutterite infants, with their normal uncontrolled impulses, into conformist Hutterite adults in the course of its educational and socialization process. The quality of adjustment did not seem to be greatly impaired by the fact that contemporary Hutterites are exposed to strong pressures for social change and assimilation as a result of their increasingly frequent contacts with the "outside world." Individuals in the group seemed to derive considerable support in making what were to them fairly satisfactory adjustments to these new social forces through controlled acculturation. When the pressure for change became too strong and Hutterite rules were violated widely enough to threaten respect for law and order, leaders often initiated a formal change of the rules before there were too many rule-breakers. Hutterite individuals could retreat from a weakly held belief and adopt practices current in the larger American society without having to break with their community. Unlike most other American minority group members, they could adapt themselves to major changes while enjoying positive group sanctions.

The quantitative approach to the study of the cultural and social aspects of mental disorders was also useful. It provided possibly significant clues which were the point of departure for more detailed clinical investigations. Frequency data cannot in themselves prove the validity of a theory, particularly since no group has a really adequate record of the occurrence of mental disorders in its population. And official statistics of patients in mental hospitals are almost worthless for this purpose; they leave out patients who have recovered and many mentally ill persons who have never come to the attention of a doctor. The Hutterite study attempted to track down every case, past or present, hospitalized or not, throughout the entire population. It probably succeeded in finding almost all the cases of psychosis and epilepsy and the severe cases of mental deficiency. Studies of similar design in nine other areas of the world were also reviewed. It was possible to adjust their frequency rates for a few of their differences, but the studies were comparable to a limited degree only, for they still varied greatly in their methods. The researchers had to use the vaguely defined diagnostic categories of psychiatry. They can be measured only crudely and significant quantitative differences are not likely to show up unless two groups vary greatly. It is logical to expect that only major causal patterns would have a sufficiently great impact on a crudely measured index such as the lifetime morbidity rate. It is doubtful that the etiological impact of minor social and cultural patterns, particularly if they are not well integrated throughout the social system can be measured or estimated quantitatively.

While quantitative differences need not be significant, for sampling error and other spurious factors may account for them, they warrant investigation. They may be significant! The history of epidemiology or medical ecology, that is, the study of the distribution of disease symptoms in a population, shows that many important discoveries were made when quantitative clues were investigated clinically to see how significant they might be. The relatively high proportion of depressive symptoms among Hutterite mental patients, and the moderate frequency of mental deficiency and epilepsy in a group which has practiced in-group mating for many generations, are probably not statistical accidents. The most clear-cut quantitative finding was the virtual absence of severe personality disorders, obsessive-compulsive neuroses, psychopathology, and psychoses associated with syphilis, alcoholism, and drug addiction. The almost complete prevention of these disorders may be possible within an appropriate social and cultural setting. The Hutterite study represents an extreme in its use of unofficial and nonprofessional informants in the case finding process. If we had used the operational definition of most official statistics—"persons admitted to a mental hospital" —or of the New Haven Study of Psychiatric Disorders—"persons under treatment by a psychiatrist"[126]—no Hutterites would have been counted as "ill" at the time our field work was done.

While no simple generalizations can be drawn for the larger society, the study of the Hutterites adds weight to the widely accepted idea that the true frequency of mental disorders in the general population, including patients *not* in hospitals and *not* under psychiatric care, is far greater than reported in any official statistical report of the past. Americans have more mental disorders than are publicly recorded. The true dimensions of this public health problem are yet to be determined.

The interpretation that sociological variables can explain a great deal about symptoms of Hutterite mental health cannot be generalized to apply equally to less cohesive societies. It is doubtful that parents and groups in more diversified social systems can greatly influence the risk of psychotic breakdown through minor, temporary, and sometimes contradictory reforms. As has been pointed out previously, this theory has an optimistic implication. It follows that a great deal of cumulative stress and/or traumatic impact is necessary to increase the number of functional psychoses in a human group. No child can be "ruined" by occasional parental or group thoughtlessness. But there is also a more sobering caution. Large-scale preventive mental hygiene programs are not likely to show quick and dramatic effects that can be demonstrated statistically. They are not likely to be effective at all unless they are well integrated and supported throughout the entire social system. Preventive mental hygiene would not appear to be a job for piecemeal social action. The home, the school, the place of work, and other social institutions need to work on an integrated long-range program if it is to have a measurable effect. There are no "quickie" techniques in the battle for mental health.

It is doubtful that our study would have been productive of many clues to how social and cultural variables are related to various mental disorders if the Hutterite social system had been less homogeneous and integrated. Without the many well defined sociological attributes which distinguish nearly all Hutterites from most of their fellow Americans and from the people in other areas where mental disorder studies were made, the net impact of these sociological variables would probably have been too small to be detected in an epidemiological study.

The Hutterites provide us with a good example of the

mental health significance of ideology and beliefs. Their importance is not often denied at the theoretical level, but it is sometimes ignored by practitioners in the process of therapy. "Religion?" is, as has been said, one of the routine questions asked when a person is admitted to a mental hospital, and this item of information is used largely to arrange for appropriate last rites if the person should die while in the hospital's jurisdiction. Formal religious affiliations are not important for personality dynamics but strongly held faiths are. From the therapeutic point of view religion can be both a positive and negative mental health element. It gives many Hutterites a sense of great security but is also responsible for the high frequency of guilt feelings. Our study supports the conclusion that religious convictions are likely to be important factors in the symptomatic manifestations of mental disorders, as well as in their treatment. If this hypothesis is correct, we should find differences in frequency and typology of psychotic symptoms by religious conviction rather than by formal affiliation. Orthodox Jews or devout Catholics should show different symptoms from those who are less orthodox in the same faiths. Such distinctions are likely to be missed in any study which breaks down cases into statistical categories based on formal rather than functional religious identification. In general, there has been adequate recognition in psychiatry of the fact that genetic, somatic, and psychological factors have a bearing on mental disorders. There is increasing acceptance of the theory that social relations are related to the manifestations of mental stress. The importance of culture, of the faiths, hopes, and fears which are produced in group living and transmitted from generation to generation, also needs to be fully recognized.

The theory that sociological factors are related to mental disorders is potentially controversial. Individuals and groups with whom a patient is closely associated sometimes react emotionally against the theory as if it were an accusation of

guilt. This factor may have a great deal to do with the preference of many people for genetic and organic theories of
etiology. The reality of this widespread antisociological bias
was well illustrated when the study of the Hutterites and
their mental health was announced publicly by the National
Institute of Mental Health, which provided most of its financial support. Serious question was raised in some quarters
concerning the appropriateness of financial sponsorship of
such a study by a governmental research fund. Apprehen-
sion was expressed along the following line: "Do you want
to prove that these strange people have a better approach to
life than the majority of Americans? Is the government
spending money to get more people to live like Hutterites in
isolated communities, give up capitalism for communal ownership of property, and refuse to bear arms?" The same type of
bias was shown by those Hutterites who first approached our
study with the hope that it implied recognition of what they
regard as the superiority of their way of life over the "wicked
ways of the world."

Our study leaves many questions unanswered. We have
explored hypotheses about the dynamic consequences of certain culture traits and social relationships for mental health
and disorder, but many of these involve post factum explanations. They are plausible, and at times they seem to be impressively convincing because of the internal consistency of
much of our data and those of other investigators. Post factum explanations, however, can never inspire a high degree
of confidence. Other hypotheses which might also be consistent with the data could not be systematically checked.
This study, therefore, also demonstrates the inadequacy of a
purely social and cultural approach to mental health problems. The case histories of Hutterite patients were inadequate for a systematic examination of psychological and life-
history variables. Social-genetic drift cannot be ruled out as
an explanation of some of our findings. It was not possible for

our staff to include the study of genetic problems in this investigation. The historical and religious factors which have made the Hutterites a culturally distinct and homogeneous group may also have produced an unusual concentration of certain genetically transmitted tendencies.

Frequency variations in mental disorders are an important first step in the attainment of new knowledge, but they do not explain *why* and *how* these variations occur. Our study confirms indications by many previous epidemiological investigations that social and cultural categories such as age, sex, role expectations, and social cohesion are correlated with the frequency of certain mental disorders in a population. There are many dynamic clues in our data, but they also highlight how far we have to travel beyond the present stage of hypothesis formulation to the goal of hypothesis testing. Questions of the specific relationship of sociological variables and symptoms of mental disorders are largely unexplored. This area in psychiatry must be mapped before much progress can be expected in applying quantitative sociological findings to the planning of psychiatric prevention and treatment programs. They are next on the agenda of urgent business in mental health research.

In about two decades, when another generation of Hutterites has lived through maturity, the validity of our sociological interpretations can, to some extent, be tested. In view of our findings and their interpretations, we would predict no substantial change in the quantitative and qualitative data on mental disorders if there is no major change in the social cohesiveness and cultural life of the sect. However, there are many indications of selective acceptance by the Hutterites of the values and practices of the larger American society. If this assimilatory process continues, our data and sociocultural hypotheses would support the following predictions:

Psychoses:

There will be a moderate increase in frequency, with a larger proportion of schizophrenic and a smaller proportion of manic-depressive reaction cases. There will also be an increase in chronic brain disorders associated with alcoholism and old age. More cases of suicide can be expected to occur during the 20-year period.

Psychoneurosis:

There will be a considerable increase in frequency, with a smaller proportion of patients who show severely depressive symptoms and the appearance of individuals with free-floating anxiety and dissociative, phobic, and obsessive-compulsive reactions. There will be much more malingering and evasion of work responsibilities than there was in 1951.

Personality Disorders:

There will be a considerable increase in the frequency of antisocial acts committed by Hutterites, against both their own and the larger American social system. Violations of moral norms, particularly those related to sex, personal violence, and private property, are likely to occur. More Hutterites will commit violations of laws which will bring them into contact with American courts and penal institutions. Many more Hutterites will have made a permanent break with their community, and they will include more women than in 1951. There will be more overt family conflict, and a greater number of cases of desertion or divorce can be expected to occur during the 20-year period.

Mental Defects:

There will be no great change in the frequency of severe and moderate cases, although better prenatal and obstetric care may result in the prevention of some birth injury cases. The number of mild mental defect cases will increase as the community becomes less protective of its membership and as individuals experience more difficulties in making an adjustment between the conflicting expectation of some of the Hutterite and the general American social values.

Epilepsy:

There will be no change in the frequency.

These gloomy predictions will affect only a small proportion of the entire sect, although it will be larger than the 2-1/3 per cent of the population who were enumerated in 1951 as having been mentally disordered at some time. On the other hand, there is no evidence that would warrant a prediction that the entire sect will break up and a large proportion of its membership will show severe symptoms of personal or social disorganization. There will be a greater participation by Hutterites in the American economic, intellectual, and (to a smaller degree) political life. A wider occupational choice will be available to Hutterite youngsters. The general standard of living will rise. Women will have opportunities to engage in activities now reserved almost exclusively to men; they will have fewer children but they will be able to give them a great deal more individual attention. The Hutterite flexibility of responding to strong pressures for social change through controlled acculturation provides a basis for optimism that the sect may be able to maintain some of the present social framework, which provides considerable psychological, economic, and group support for its membership.

The history of the Amana Colony in Iowa illustrates that this is a realistic expectation. Most of the shareholders and employees of the *Amana Corporation* (deepfreezer units, air-conditioners, refrigerators, furniture, blankets, and farm products) lived very much as the Hutterites do, as recently as

1932. At that time these sponsors of a national radio-TV program ("People Are Funny") would not allow a radio in their home! They lived in a communitarian arrangement. They maintained their isolated and cohesive way of life in America for 99 years. When the pressures for assimilation had become very intense, and when the younger people failed to respond appropriately to the bonds of faith, tradition, language, and kinship which had kept their ancestors together, the group decided unanimously to reorganize on a more individualistic basis. The old Amana is no more, but the inhabitants of these prosperous Iowa villages have joined the mainstream of America without widespread social pathology or individual demoralization.

These predictions have been written down because of a conviction that prediction is an important criterion of validity. Social science knowledge cannot be regarded as being adequate until it can be used to make forecasts with some degree of confidence. However, we must not expect all such predictions to come true, even if the generalizations are valid. There are other etiological variables which can, and probably will, counteract the sociological trends that have been anticipated. For example, medical science may discover new ways of treating mental disorders and thus reduce the frequency of psychoses, some psychoneuroses, and many mental defects. This development would make invisible the quantitative effect of sociological factors. Many other events, unanticipated at present, are likely to occur which will affect the findings 20 years hence. It is even conceivable that this book will help to motivate some Hutterite parents, teachers, and leaders to adopt psychological practices and take social action to prevent the realization of these predictions. By calling attention to the probable impact on personality of change in their social and cultural system, Hutterites, and the professional persons whom they consult about mental disorders, can plan a mental hygiene program. They might learn to meet the problems of social change as effectively as they have dealt with the problems of the status quo.

Prediction is the best criterion of validity in the physical sciences; in the social sciences, the usefulness of this criterion is limited because men have a veto power over some of the forces which shape their fate, which the remainder of the universe does not have. Human beings *can say an effective "No" to many a generalization!* They have the intellectual and emotional power to bring about a creative modification of their own environment. Much of the support for social science research comes from the hope that it can anticipate social trends regarded as undesirable, so that their realization can be prevented. Men need not wait upon nature to evolve a mutation; they can produce it.

Research Procedures

What Is a Case?

No study is better than the raw material used to make it. As researchers proceed with the analysis of their information, they deal with refined results of a long "production" process. Along its route many decisions of a technical nature are made about field work organization, observational techniques, sampling, and record keeping. They may mean little to anyone but the specialist, but they are crucial for the validity of the conclusions.

One of the important methodological problems in our study was the criteria used to distinguish between "normal" people and psychiatric "cases." Active and severe maladjustments create no great diagnostic problem. An incontinent idiot will be recognized as mentally defective by almost anyone; a catatonic schizophrenic also is not likely to be diagnosed as "normal." Even in such instances of severe pathology, experts sometimes disagree in their differential diagnosis. In milder cases it becomes more difficult to distinguish between persons who have a normal reaction to stress and those who respond in a pathological manner. No neat boundary can be drawn between a normal anxiety reaction and an anxiety neurosis, between a neurotic depression and a psychotic depression. The beginning and end of an illness are also often so gradual that their delineation in time is more or less arbitrary. There are, in fine, no generally acceptable criteria of mental health or disorder. No person is fully "normal" at all times. The idea was well stated by Ernest Jones:

We have no experience of a completely normal mind. Is there any reason to suppose that a mind could be ideally normal? We do not meet absolute perfection elsewhere in the universe, even in Newton's Law of Motion. It would be astonishing to find it in such a wry locality as the mind of man.[127]

The question of psychiatric case definition was the topic for discussion at a scientific meeting sponsored by the Milbank Fund, attended by representatives of several American research projects on the epidemiology of mental illness. None had a satisfactory answer.[128] Nor could they agree on a "best" criterion. Their criteria for determining the existence and duration of a "case" differed widely.

In the Hutterite study, any individual was counted if he was diagnosed as having been mentally disordered at any time from birth to August 31, 1951, provided he was alive on December 31, 1950, when our population census was made. Both active and recovered cases were included. The duration of illness was not considered in the case count, nor was any person counted more than once, even if he had experienced more than one attack of mental disorder. Those who had died before December 31, 1950, were separately enumerated and excluded from the calculation of lifetime morbidity rates. The time of exposure to the risk of becoming ill was the cumulative total of all life spans of individuals in the population prior to the date on which the study was completed.

All diagnoses were made by the psychiatrist, in consultation with the sociologist. There also were conferences with other field staff members who had participated in the gathering of information, particularly about cases where there were difficulties in the differential diagnosis. The psychiatrist personally examined one-third of the cases. Nonmedical members of our research staff saw most of these same patients and an additional 22 per cent. About 44 per cent of the cases were not seen by any member of the staff. They were diagnosed on the basis of secondary data, the sources of which will be detailed later. Five major categories were used: Psychoses, Psychoneuroses, Mental Defects, Epilepsy, and Personality Disorder. Cases were categorized as active, improved, or recovered, on the basis of their condition during the summer of 1951 when the last phase of our field work was completed. Social adjustment was an important factor in this evaluation.

Each case was reviewed at least twice. A diagnosis was made in the fall of 1951 on the basis of the nosological definitions given by James Coleman.[129] In July, 1952, after the American Psychiatric Association *Diagnostic and Statistical Manual*[130] had been published, all cases were rediagnosed to conform to its nosological categories. The decision to rediagnose was made for two reasons: First, in many cases new information had been obtained. Correspondence with patients, colony leaders, and doctors had provided facts which reduced the degree of uncertainty and, in some cases, changed the original diagnosis. Second, we wanted our categories to be as comparable as possible to those of future studies; the new *Manual* is likely to become standard for most future psychiatric surveys.

Those who were ill with severe organic symptoms, gross emotional difficulties, or poor social adjustment generally stood out clearly. Many of the patients recognized that they were ill; if they did not, their relatives and the community usually did. The Hutterites gave information in every case, although more detailed entries in field notes were made only if these lay sources provided information which was new to the staff, as occurred in 87 per cent of the cases. We also received many leads from two census questionnaires sent to all Hutterite colonies at the end of 1949 and 1950. Hospital records contributed to the histories of about 21 per cent of all patients. Doctors in private practice furnished information on 29 per cent of the cases.

Our policy was to accept the clinically more severe of equally plausible diagnoses. For example, a depressed person, if the evidence was insufficient to determine definitely whether he was neurotic or psychotic, was classified as suffering from a manic-depressive reaction. A mental defective with epilepsy was listed as primarily defective. This bias in favor of morbidity was adopted because our study was made to test the hypothesis that the Hutterites were relatively free from severe mental illnesses.

Individual records were kept for each of the 199 persons diagnosed by our staff as having had a mental disorder or epileptic seizure at some time. An additional 56 suspected cases were investigated, but when all information was in they were diagnosed as *not* mentally ill.* Persons who were born in a Hutterite colony but became ill after they had severed their connection with it were included; converts who had joined the sect as adults, and their children, were excluded.

Field Work Staff

The findings of a mental disorder survey depend on more than the morbidity in the population; they are also a function of the fact that the recording "devices," the research staff, and the objects of study—mental patients—are human beings and cannot be fully standardized. There can be little of the

---

* As has been pointed out above, there was considerable doubt in our mind regarding the validity of including epileptic persons in our survey of mental illnesses. The 20 persons diagnosed in our study as epileptic were *without* psychotic or mental defective traits. There is no more justification for counting them than for counting other neurological conditions, such as disseminated sclerosis. We did so only for reasons of comparability. Past census surveys of mental disorders have included epileptics.

precision possible in the measurement of temperature or speed or voltage. The size of the research staff, their academic backgrounds, their personalities, their theoretical orientation, and the setting in which the observations were made are significant variables in the design of any social science study.

The project was directed by the senior author, a sociologist. He became acquainted with a Hutterite colony in 1941, while making a study of the socioeconomic aspects of cooperative farming.[131] He proposed the research project in 1949 to the National Institute of Mental Health of the United States Public Health Service, which provided financial support for the study. Some of the field research phase planning, once the professional staff had been selected, was done by a senior field research team, including the writers and two psychologists, Bert Kaplan and Thomas F. A. Plaut, who spent approximately 18 man months in the field during the summers of 1950 and 1951. Six graduate students, most of them with a background in sociology, also participated in the field research. They spent about 26 man months in Hutterite colonies and neighboring areas. One of them lived in a Hutterite colony for nine months and was employed by the provincial school board as teacher of the one-room grade school.

In many anthropological investigations of communities, a single investigator goes into the field. While he is gathering the data, he is usually isolated from other professionals, who might see things that escape his attention or come to different conclusions about the observed facts. In this study the close and informal working relationship of several researchers from sociology, psychiatry, and psychology makes it less likely that the findings are colored by a personal bias. Our observations were subjected to a process of interpersonal and interdisciplinary verification at their source. This fact, however, cannot be regarded as an adequate substitute for an independent test of our diagnostic judgments. Having one or more additional psychiatrists examine and diagnose the cases enumerated would have added much to the confidence in the findings of this study. An independent test of the reliability of our diagnostic judgments by someone who had not participated in the original field work was considered, but the cost in funds and staff time of such a procedure was beyond the available resources.

In the course of discussions of diagnostic problems, a joint working concept of mental health was formulated. Briefly, it was assumed that mental health and disorders can be viewed conveniently as a complex interaction of five major etiological aspects. Mental health or disorders can be manifested through symptoms in any one or several of these. The staff developed a check list of 39 indices of good and poor mental health. This was useful as a frame of reference in staff conferences, even though our case records were not sufficiently detailed to apply this instrument consistently to every Hutterite who was clinically diagnosed. Our list included indices of five aspects:

1. *Genetic*, including evidence of familial transmission, although the latter may be indicative in some cases of cultural continuity rather than genetic linkage.
2. *Organic*, including infectious, traumatic, glandular, and neurological variables.
3. *Intrapersonal*, covering basic needs and subjective and emotional factors.
4. *Interpersonal*, including the effect of all social relations.
5. *Cultural*, including the role of values, religion, and ideology.

Case Studies

The Hutterite study was initiated with the expectation that few cases of mental disorder would be found. If this had been true, each case might have been studied with a great deal of clinical depth. But when it became apparent that mental disorders were somewhat more frequent than had been antici-

pated, the choice had to be made between an extensive study
of morbidity in the entire sect and a detailed examination of a
small number of cases. The question was: Should we aim at
having good frequency tables with some clinical data to interpret them, or much clinical data for interpretation, with
no reliable frequency tables?

The choice was in favor of the first alternative. There was
no sampling; the entire population of 8,542 persons living in
a large geographical area, including parts of South Dakota,
North Dakota, Manitoba, Alberta, and Montana, was screened
for cases of mental disorders. The staff visited 84 of the 93
colonies in existence at the time the field work was completed;
the remaining nine colonies were screened through a variety
of informants.

However, our study is not devoid of clinical data useful for
an interpretation of dynamic personality processes commonly
found in this culture. We have fairly detailed histories on a
dozen mental patients and some fifty normal individuals. The
records of other persons diagnosed as having a mental disorder
are primarily summaries of pathology. They contain brief
notes on conditions that interfere with normal social, psychological, and physical functioning. They are useful for establishing a general diagnosis but insufficient for making a
differential diagnosis with a high degree of confidence. For
example, we had no difficulty in diagnosing schizophrenia but
often lacked data necessary to differentiate between sub-
classifications, such as hebephrenic type, paranoid type, catatonic type, and simple type. The close-knit communal life of
the Hutterites, with the consequent intimate knowledge that
the people have of one another, makes it probable that despite
its lack of clinical depth, this extensive survey procedure resulted in an enumeration of nearly all severe cases. This objective was further aided by the distinctiveness of Hutterite
family names, dress, and manner. Doctors, hospitals, and public officials were able to furnish information about suspected

cases, even though they kept no official records of religious affiliation.

Our staff talked to approximately 2,000 Hutterites. In addition to written field notes on a variety of topics and persons, there were 298 recorded physical examinations given by the psychiatrist. He also had cursory contacts with probably another 500 persons who came to him with requests for medical information. Thematic apperception tests were administered to about 100 persons. We also gave 12 Rorschach tests and 125 especially constructed sentence completion tests.

Wherever possible, physical examinations and psychological tests were given to the same people. However, the various study methods had differing appeal. Many adults were glad to be interviewed or to submit to a physical examination but objected to the projective tests. They did not want to "tell stories," "imagine things," or "look at silly pictures like a school kid." Older school children and young men and women tended to respond more readily to psychological tests. They were more familiar with such exercises through school examinations.

Much time was spent with what anthropologists call "good informants," including a large number of persons in positions of leadership. There also were many who were somewhat ambivalent about their way of life and were attracted to us because we were "outsiders." Persons who had been mentally or physically ill were sought out by our staff for special study. Midwives, people with more than the average secular education, colony business managers (*Bosses*), preachers, Hutterite religious teachers ("German" teachers) and persons who were old but had good memories were also of particular interest.

There was some unplanned selection of informants on the basis of personality, age, sex, and occupation. While all field workers had close personal contact with representative persons in every segment of Hutterite society, the psychiatrist found himself most appreciated by those who thought they had a "problem." One psychologist concentrated his efforts on persons who spoke English well and were willing to take psychological tests; the other psychologist, who spoke German, spent most of his time with young men and women. The study director often worked with colony leaders, who had to be approached first in accordance with Hutterite practices governing the relationship of "colony people" with "outsiders." His wife and babies were sought out by many Hutterite adolescent girls and mothers. The staff was least effective in establishing rapport with preschool children; Hutterite youngsters know little English until they are about seven or eight years old, and they do not begin to learn it well until they reach public school. Three members of the senior staff spoke modern German fluently, but they had difficulty in following verbal exchanges of young children who spoke only the Hutterite dialect. The staff relationships with Hutterites were not random, but there was an awareness during the field work that these tendencies towards selection existed and they were considered in the analysis of the data.

Mental Hospital Contacts

Official rates of mental disorder are generally based on the number of inmates in public and private mental hospitals. This case-finding procedure has the advantage that access to the data is relatively easy; hospitals lend themselves readily to statistical study. Being an inmate of a mental hospital can be used as an operational definition of psychosis, although only involuntary commitment is based on a somewhat uniform process of legal evidence and procedure. But there are great variations in hospital admission standards and diagnostic practices. Not all patients in a hospital for mental disease are psychotic. Some are committed for chronic complaints without organic findings or because they create a community problem. In 1948 a Federal summary of first admissions for mental disease in all reporting state hospitals in the United States[132] showed that 3.7 per cent of the cases were admitted with a diagnosis of psychoneurosis and 11.9 per cent without psychosis; for 10.6 per cent no mental disorder was reported, the case was unclassified, or the diagnosis was "other" or "unknown." Thus, more than one of every four new cases in 1948 in our state mental hospitals was diagnosed as without a clear-cut psychosis.

Hospital records contributed data to our case histories in 21 per cent of the cases. A nationally prominent medical center was particularly important. Despite its distance of more than 1,000 miles from many of the colonies, and the high cost of sending patients over such distance, the center had records of 103 members of the sect who had been there since 1925 for diagnosis and treatment of every type of medical problem, mostly of a nonpsychiatric nature. No member of the sect was in a mental hospital during our survey period in 1950-51; only four of the psychotic patients had even been admitted to such an institution. Inquiries were made at state hospitals in every area where Hutterites are living. The small number of Hutterite family names made it a simple matter to check through hospital files. A recheck of these hospitals in December 1953 disclosed that they still had no Hutterite patients at the time, although three members of the sect had been admitted for diagnosis and short-term treatment since our inquiry in 1950.

Physician Contacts

General practitioners of medicine see many patients with mental symptoms. Estimates of the incidence of functional illnesses range from 12 per cent to "more than half" of all cases seen by general practitioners and in general clinics.[133] These estimates are based on nothing but impressions, and they vary with the doctor's sensitivity to the psychiatric implications of illness. But there is no doubt that patients with mental illnesses are seen by every doctor, regardless of his medical specialty.

Private practitioners have been used as sources of referral in most frequency studies, including our own. Their use as informants presents many problems. Research workers require much time and they can usually pay little for it. Free time is something of which a busy doctor in private practice has little. Many keep only scanty records of their impressions, findings, and treatment, and others have little sophistication about emotional and social factors in illness. Their diagnoses may be quite misleading.

There is also a problem of medical ethics. In an epidemiological survey it is impractical to depend only on data released by consent of the actual or suspected patient. Special care must therefore be taken to protect the confidential nature of each history. Researchers who expect to use these professional sources must be ready to devote the necessary staff time to reassure each doctor regarding the ethical justification for his co-operation. It was helpful to have the backing of an institution of some general prestige, such as a university, to reduce the number of refusals of co-operation.

The experiences of private practitioners were utilized in two ways. First, a general check list* concerning Hutterite health conditions was sent to all doctors whose names were supplied by leaders of Hutterite communities. They were asked to give their *opinion* about the prevalence of 53 psychosomatic symptoms and other mental health indices with which they were likely to have had some experience in their general practice. The list also included some questions about nonprofessional contacts with Hutterites which might influence their ratings. The schedule was designed to find out whether Hut-

* The check list was prepared with the help of James Clark Moloney, M.D., as psychiatric consultant, and a panel of medical advisers, all of whom had volunteered their services. They included Martin Schaeffer, M.D.; John C. Montgomery, M.D.; Harry Jurow, M.D.; and Dwight C. Ensign, M.D.

terites' mental health is thought to be different from that of the general population. It was also hoped that some trends would be suggested that could be followed up and tested in the field. This opinion poll was not intended to be a method of establishing the validity of medical facts. A clear majority vote on a medical question does not prove that the doctors are right but there is a somewhat greater than random chance that they may be.

Fifty-five American and Canadian doctors and dentists, constituting 69 per cent of those in a position to reply, volunteered to co-operate in the mail survey. Almost half reported that they had been in professional contact with Hutterites for more than ten years. Twenty-two estimated that they had been consulted by over 100 members during the last year; eleven others had seen 50-99 Hutterites. The rest had seen fewer than 50 Hutterite patients a year.

The doctors generally expressed the opinion that there was a significant difference in symptomatology between their Hutterite and non-Hutterite patients. The Hutterites appeared to them to have fewer psychosomatic symptoms. The reliability of the following clinical judgments that "Hutterites have *less*" of these symptoms was significant at the 0.01 level of confidence:*

Chronic insomnia	Hay fever
Chronic use of sleeping pills	Suicides, including attempts
Drug addiction	Complaints of poor appetite
Extreme alcoholism	Urinary tract infections
Nervous tics	Syphilis
Fainting	Male impotence
Hysterical seizures	Interest in birth control infor-
Asthma	mation
Food allergies	Fear of death

The following clinical judgments that "Hutterites have

---

* The procedure for statistical analysis based on the null hypothesis was suggested by Dr. Benjamin Epstein of the Department of Mathematics of Wayne University.

less" than the general population were significant at the 0.05 level of confidence:

Chronic nightmares   Coronary heart disease
Amnesia   Malingering

The clinical judgments that "Hutterites have *more* of the symptoms than non-Hutterite patients in our practice" were significant at the 0.01 level of confidence:

Obesity   Capacity to endure pain
Fats in the diet

The judgments concerning other physical conditions and psychological syndromes generally supported the thesis that there is a difference in physical and mental health between the general population and the Hutterites. The opinions generally favored the latter, but not at a .05 level of confidence. They included opinions that Hutterites had:

Less nailbiting   Less female frigidity
Less stuttering after the age of   Less aggressiveness in personal
  eight or among adults   relationships
Less chronic headaches   Less worry about illness
Less nightwalking   Less feelings of personal in-
Less cancer   adequacy
Less chronic constipation   Less parental emphasis on
Less spastic colitis   early toilet training
Less chronic digestive disturb-   More salt in diet
  ances   More arterial hypertension
Less kidney malfunctions   over the age of 40
Less hypertensive complica-   More general good physical
  tions in pregnancy   health
Less complaint of menstrual   More general good mental
  disorders   health

Little or no difference between Hutterites and the general population was thought to exist in the following:

Hypochondriac complaints   Dependability in personal
Arteriosclerosis   relationships

Average life expectancy   Arterial hypertension under
Chronic bedwetting after the   the age of 40
   age of six   Eczema

Specific inquiries were also made of doctors about individual cases known to them. Much of this consultation was done by mail. Doctors in private practice contributed to the histories of 29 per cent of all enumerated patients.

Public Agency Contacts

Patients with mental problems often become known to nonmedical informants long before a doctor is consulted. Courts, social work agencies, the police, and public health nurses may have contact with mentally ill persons. Ministers, lawyers, and teachers may see individuals who have a psychiatric problem. In urban areas, consulting psychologists, marriage counsellors, and vocational guidance specialists see a fair number of persons with psychiatric difficulties.

Many local welfare and police officials were approached by our study staff. Some reported: "As fare as I or anyone in this office can recall, we have had no contact with these people." Others had to inform us that "in accordance with a long-standing policy, our files are confidential and available for official use only." Generally, few of the officials had psychiatrically relevant experiences with Hutterites. No member of the sect seemed to have requested relief or any other form of public assistance. We found no instance of major crime.

Our staff made contact with five lawyers frequently consulted by colony leaders. They were quite conversant with Hutterite social customs and legal problems but knew little about the emotional problems of individual members. The absence of intimate contact with individual members was even more apparent in government officials, such as county superintendents of schools or public health nurses. Sometimes there was a conflict between what these officials regarded as "their duty under the law" and what the Hutterites regarded as "their duty unto God." Among the most valuable non-Hutterite informants were the English teachers in colony schools, most of whom live in colonies during the school months. Unfortunately, most of our field work was done during the summer months, when the schools were closed. Many of the regular teachers were then attending summer school or otherwise unavailable.

Hutterite Contacts

Mental health and illness are matters of intimate personal concern. Members of the family, neighbors, friends, employers, or fellow workers are often well informed about the condition of a case. These close associates generally have strong feelings about the person, which influence their perception and willingness to impart information to strongers. Some will consciously withhold pertinent facts because they regard matters related to mental illness as "dirty linen," not to be washed in public. There may be little of the insight into the meaning of behavior such as is more often found in professional informants. But their close association with the patient warrants every possible effort to consult these informants if maximum accuracy is to be attained in a study. Often there are difficulties in establishing rapport with these primary group informants. Each person must be approached separately in terms of his capacity to understand the study and his personal needs, which must be satisfied to some extent if he is to co-operate.

The intimacy of Hutterite communal life greatly simplified this process. Once a few leading families and colonies had begun to co-operate, nearly everyone else fell into line. We did not have to "sell" our study to every informant. There was a transfer of rapport from family to family, colony to colony, and kinship group to kinship group. While we did not speak to or examine every one of the 8,542 Hutterites, probably there were few individuals not well known to at least a dozen persons who helped us in the case count. The wide network of intimate personal knowledge throughout the culture is the main reason for assuming that few severely ill or disordered mental patients could have been missed. Our contacts with individual communities were either intensive or extensive. The former were designed to give our staff a normative picture of mental health and illness in a few "typical" colonies. The latter had the purpose of enumerating mental disorders in the entire culture.

The field work began with an intensive study of five Hutterite villages in the summer of 1950. These colonies were selected for study because their leaders appeared to be most ready to co-operate effectively. They were located on good highways and belonged to two different kinship groups. Nothing was known about the mental state of their membership. The idea of choosing on a strictly random basis was considered but rejected. Ease in doing the field work seemed to be more important than randomness in choice, in view of the relative similarity of all colonies. An attempt was made to meet and examine every person in these five colonies. The recorded contacts, as shown in Table 20, include 187 physical

Table 20—Percentage of Persons by Age and Sex Groups in Five Hutterite Colonies with a Recorded Contact with the Research Staff
(Population as of July 1950)

AGE BRACKET	MALE		FEMALE		TOTAL	
	Number of Persons in 5 Colonies	Percentage Contacted	Number of Persons in 5 Colonies	Percentage Contacted	Number of Persons	Percentage
0-14	88	31	78	53	166	41
15-24	30	77	31	97	61	87
25-34	27	89	23	91	50	90
35-44	15	93	16	94	31	94
45-59	12	83	10	80	22	82
60 & over	6	100	5	80	11	91
Total	178	58	163	73	341	65

examinations, 75 thematic apperception tests, 72 sentence completion tests, 10 Rorschach tests, and general biographical information on 227 persons. The coverage of women was more complete than that of men. The former were more accessible than their menfolk, who often worked in the field during the day and came home fatigued at night. In most age groups it was possible to examine almost nine out of ten persons. Among children under the age of 15, only about four in ten were examined. Most of those missed were under ten years of age; these youngsters do not speak English fluently and are quite shy with strangers. A few parents also refused permission to interview their youngsters or to give them psychological tests, for fear that they might get "bad ideas." Most of the people not interviewed or examined by our staff were, however, observed in their homes, the kindergarten, the community dining room, or in other colony settings.

Our staff had frequent and intimate associations with a great number of individuals in an additional 14 colonies, although no attempt was made to do a similarly complete screening job of the entire membership. Colonies in this category also were not chosen at random. Two factors played a role in their selection: the presence of good informants and/or active cases of psychosis. These 19 colonies with 1,671 inhabitants, or 19 per cent of the Hutterite population, were visited by most of the senior staff. It is very unlikely that any cases of mental disorder were missed in this category of intensively studied colonies.

The remaining 74 colonies were studied by less intensive methods. Sixty-five were visited briefly. They had a population of 6,123, or 72 per cent of the sect. Most of these settlements were visited only two or three times, and some only once. The staff relied largely on the co-operation of preachers, teachers, managers, midwives, ex-patients, or families of patients to obtain information. But information about these colonies was frequently verified through informants in other communities. Some cases of pathology may have been missed, particularly if the patients had mild symptoms or had completely recovered at the time the enumeration was made.

Nine colonies were not visited by any member of the staff. They had a population of 748 persons, or nine per cent of the sect. Their geographical location was the most important reason for their neglect. In most cases it would have been necessary to travel on poor roads for two or three hundred additional miles. Considerable information about these colonies had been obtained from their friends and relatives in other colonies.

Each colony was visited with a prepared "shopping list" of leads about persons suspected of being of interest to our study. We also had knowledge of who might be good informants. Demonstration of such knowledge helped to motivate informants to fill out details unknown to us. For example: "I see they already told you about Wild Fred, but you are wrong about some of the facts. You had better get the story straight." We made it a special point to question informants about their knowledge of psychiatric cases in other communities.

We had more help from Hutterite ministers than from anyone else. Every colony elects one or two of its members to serve as lay preachers. It is part of their social role to meet visitors, and they are generally well informed. Many of the preachers showed considerable understanding of our study. There were few outright refusals to co-operate with us, although there were wide variations in the sensitivity of different ministers to the emotional problems of their "flock." All Hutterites (including children) are required to confess their "sins" to the preachers; without such a confession atonement cannot be attained. While Hutterite ministers are not permitted to divulge the details of acts about which they learn during a confession, they were able to indicate which individuals had "lots of conscience trouble" or to explain "He's not well, you know." Preachers also had intimate knowledge of possible psychiatric cases in colonies other than their own. They do a good deal of traveling between colonies, because their position carries certain administrative responsibilities. They are the "central wires" of the Hutterite hearsay system of communication.

In most of our dealing with informants, no formal questionnaire was used. The staff formulated a list of topics, which were discussed whenever it was appropriate. They were memorized and were never put to any individual at one sitting. They included the following areas:

I. In the area of genetic background.
    1. Among your ancestors who was born defective or ill?
    2. Among your ancestors who developed a mental illness while he was alive?
    3. When was the defect or illness first noted? At birth, in childhood, after an accident or a shock?

II. In the area of physical health.
    1. Who is crippled or has a severe or incurable disease?
    2. Who has high blood pressure?
    3. Who gets spells during which he does not act naturally?
    4. Who is sick a lot and thinks a lot of "doctoring" is needed?
    5. Who goes to a chiropractor or frequents herb-doctors because he has no faith in regular doctors?
    6. Who mixes up his words so that you cannot understand what he is saying?
    7. Who finds it hard to sleep at night?

III. In the area of intrapersonal relations.
    1. Who sees things that are not there?

2. Who likes to make up stories about things that could never happen?

3. Who is often depressed or unhappy, or rarely laughs?

4. Whom has fate given a hard life?

5. Who is frightened easily or has fears of specific things and people?

6. Who gets upset easily—who has a bad temper?

7. Is there anybody with a troubled mind?

8. Who fears people will do bad things?

9. Who blames other people most of the time when things don't go right?

10. Who could not do well in English school or German (religious) school?

11. Who is nervous? (*Nervisch.*)

12. Who is tempted by the devil? (*Anfechtung.*)

13. Who is always willing to let other people tell him what to do?

14. Who can hardly sit still and relax—who always has to be on the go?

15. Who lost his mind?

IV. In the area of interpersonal relationships.

1. Who has left the colony and why?

2. Who is over 30 years of age and is not married?

3. Is there any older married couple without children?

4. Is there any couple where there is a lot of conflict in the family?

5. Is there any couple who have so much work and trouble with their children that they can hardly manage them like the other colony people do?

6. Who can't stand having children around?

7. Is there anyone who has to disagree with almost everything?

8. Who is very shy and does not like to mix with people?

9. Who is causing the colony a lot of trouble?

10. Is there anyone in the colony who has committed a crime?

11. Who does not do his share of the work or cannot be trusted to work alone?

12. Is there any adult who is not baptized?

13. Is there anybody of whom other people are afraid?

14. Who likes to fight with people?

15. Is there anybody who enjoys being mean to others?

V. In the area of relations of culture and values.

1. Who is too religious and tries to reform everybody else?

2. Is there anybody who feels he doesn't live right?

3. Is there anybody who does not go to church much?

4. Is there anybody who is or ever has been excommunicated from the church and from normal social contact with other brothers and sisters?

5. Is there anybody who is too worldly?

Genetic Methods

The European epidemiological surveys of mental disorders tend to make use of the proband method of case finding. A proband is a person affected by a disease whose detection leads to a study of his family, in addition to himself. Under "family" one usually includes children, siblings, and parents of the proband, but some researchers have studied an even wider range of relationships. This method is commonly used in studies in which familial or genetic factors are thought to be important. The proband method can also be used as a control sample on the completeness of coverage of a census type survey. If the census is complete, a more detailed check on the relatives of all patients should discover no new cases.*

Our time in the field was too brief to allow us to make any proband checks in the Hutterite survey except in one case in which the method was used because of a seemingly high frequency of mental illnesses in the family. Our staff was generally impressed by the frequency of statements by Hutterites about blood relationships between mentally disordered persons. The genetic significance of these impressions is uncertain. A thorough genetic study of the entire group will be necessary to determine their significance.

The technically interested reader or researcher can use these methodological details as points of reference for evaluating the findings and interpretations. We have indicated that this study was made within definite limits imposed by our knowledge, funds, staff time, and Hutterite attitudes. These limits often had the consequence of requiring the making of methodological compromises at the expense of ideal research procedure. Some of the technical difficulties in our social-psychiatric research were inevitable because the human behavior sciences are still in their infancy. We had experience with most of the obstacles set forth in the report of *The Committee on Psychopathology of the Group for the Advancement of Psychiatry*, which addressed itself to the question why "in few medical specialties is research more acutely needed than in psychiatry," and commented that "perhaps no

---

* Three basic approaches are possible in the application of the proband method of studying mental disorders. First, probands can be all or a sample of all cases with a psychiatric problem. The latter method was used by Torsten Sjögren.[134] Second, probands can be cases selected at random or on some other basis unrelated to mental disorder. For example, Eric Strömgren used individuals receiving hospital care for tuberculosis.[135] A third fruitful method for tracing genetically significant qualities is the study of twin probands. It has been and is now being used by Franz J. Kallmann[136] in the study of schizophrenia. (It may be noted here that there were no twins in the Hutterite population with symptoms of psychiatric significance.)

comparably important area shows greater research neglect."[137]

Despite its limitations, this study is one more illustration that quantitative and qualitative research procedures can be combined to study complex problems in social psychiatry. There is a good deal of internal consistency in our findings. Some of the confidence in our conclusions also comes from the clinical experience of the staff in getting references to the same names, similar symptoms, and similar judgments in response to inquiries in many different colonies and from various sources. In most cases there was basic agreement among the four major categories of persons who contributed data used by the psychiatrist to make a diagnosis, in consultation with other members of the field research staff: 1) family and community; 2) patients; 3) doctors and hospitals; 4) non-Hutterite acquaintances of a patient. These informants shared a frame of reference which was sufficiently similar to facilitate a common judgment about health or disorder in an individual who was at either extreme of the mental health spectrum. But the staff alone was responsible for the diagnostic decision of where to draw the line between health and disorder, and for the judgment of which diagnostic classification was the most appropriate for a given case. It was, therefore, reassuring to learn that a pilot study of blood types made in three South Dakota Hutterite colonies in 1953 by a geneticist and hematologist, who had access to all of our data, failed to find any case of psychopathology, ill at or before the time of our investigation, that had been missed in our case-finding process.

References

1. Herbert Goldhamer and Andrew W. Marshall, *Psychosis and Civilization* (Glencoe, Ill.: Free Press, 1953).

2. Carney Landis and James D. Page, *Modern Society and Mental Disease* (New York: Farrar and Rinehart, Inc., 1939), p. 25.

3. Group for the Advancement of Psychiatry, No. 7 (Topeka, March, 1949).

4. Charles Schlaifer, "Statement Before the Bureau of the Budget, United States Government, May 27, 1952," *Memorandum of the National Mental Health Committee* (New York).

5. Robert P. Parsons, "Joseph Goldberger and Pellagra," *Great Adventures in Medicine*, ed. Samuel Rapport and Helen Wright (New York: Dial Press, 1952), pp. 586-605.

6. For a recent review and evaluation of this approach see: Ernest M. Gruenberg, "The Epidemiology of Mental Disease," *Scientific American*, Vol. 190, No. 3 (March, 1954), 38-42.

7. Lawrence K. Frank, *Society as the Patient* (New Brunswick: Rutgers University Press, 1949), p. 1.

8. Read Bain, "Our Schizoid Culture," *Sociology and Social Research*, Vol. 19 (Jan.-Feb., 1935), 266.

9. Emile Durkheim, *Suicide: A Study in Sociology*, trans. from the French by John A. Spaulding and George Simpson (Glencoe, Ill.: Free Press, 1951).

10. Robert K. Merton, *Social Theory and Social Structure* (Glencoe, Ill.: Free Press, 1949). See especially Chapter IV, "Social Structure and Anomie."

11. Ralph Linton, *The Cultural Background of Personality* (New York: Appleton-Century Co., 1945); S. Stansfeld Sargent and Marion W. Smith, eds., *Culture and Personality* (New York: Viking Fund, 1949).

12. Jurgen Reusch and Gregory Bateson, *Communication: The Social Matrix of Psychiatry* (New York: W. W. Norton & Co., 1951), p. 79.

13. James Clark Moloney, *The Battle for Mental Health* (New York: Philosophical Library, 1952), pp. 36-37.

14. S. Kirson Weinberg, *Society and Personality Disorders* (New York: Prentice Hall, 1952), pp. 228-232, 255-258.

15. Franz J. Kallman, *Heredity in Health and Mental Disorder* (New York: W. W. Norton & Co., 1953).

16. H. Bentley Glass, "The Genetics of the Dunkers," *Scientific American*, Vol. 189, No. 2 (August, 1953), 76-81.

17. Carney Landis and James D. Page, "Trends in Mental Disease," *The Journal of Abnormal and Social Psychology*, Vol. 38 (1943), 524.

18. This definition of ethnic group follows that of Robin Williams, *Reduction of Intergroup Tensions* (New York: Social Science Research Council, 1947), p. 42.

19. Many of the historical details were furnished by A. J. F. Zieglschmid, a German linguist who edited the printing of the Hutterite handwritten chronicles. He was working on a historical manuscript until his death in 1950. For more detailed accounts of Hutterite history see: A. J. F. Zieglschmid, ed., *Das Klein Geschichtsbuch der Hutterischen Brüder* (Philadelphia: The Carl Schurz Memorial Foundation, Inc., 1947); *Die Alteste Chronik der Hutterischen Brüder* (Ithaca: The Carl Schurz Memorial Foundation, Inc., 1943). For historical reports in English see: John Horsch, *The Hutterian Brethren* (Goshen, Ind.: Mennonite Historical Society, 1931); J. M. Hofer, "The Historical Background of the Hutterite Colonies, 1528-1946," *Proceedings of the Fifth Annual Conference on Mennonite Cultural Problems* [held at Freeman, South Dakota, August 27-28, 1946, under auspices of the Council of Mennonite and Affiliated Colleges] (Berne, Ind.: The Berne Witness), pp. 25-43.

20. Robert E. L. Faris and H. Warren Dunham, *Mental Disorders in Urban Areas* (Chicago: University of Chicago Press, 1939), pp. 163-164.

21. Joseph W. Eaton and Albert J. Mayer, "Social Biology of Very High Fertility," *Human Biology*, Vol. 25, No. 3 (1953), 206-264; republished under the title: *Man's Capacity to Reproduce* (Glencoe, Ill.: Free Press, 1954).

22. Bertha W. Clark, "The Hutterian Communities," *Journal of Political Economy*, Vol. 32, No. 4 (1924), 357-374, 468-486.

23. Lee Emerson Deets, *The Hutterites: A Study of Social Cohesion* (Gettysburg: *Times* and *News* Publishing Co., 1939), p. 2.

24. *The Bulletin of the Manitoba Civil Liberties Association*, Vol. 1, No. 2 (Winnipeg: Winter 1947-48), 3.

25. Marie Waldner, "The Present Day Social Customs and Culture Patterns of the Hutterites in North America," *Proceedings of the Fifth Annual Conference on Mennonite Cultural Problems* (Freeman, South Dakota: Freeman College, August, 1946).

26. Horsch, *op. cit.*, pp. 66-68.

27. Marcus Bach, "Experiment in Contentment," *Coronet*, Vol. 20 (June, 1946), 139.

28. Dorothea Leighton and Clyde Kluckhohn, *Children of the People* (Cambridge, Mass.: Harvard University Press, 1947).

29. Carl Brugger, "Versuch einer Geisteskrankenzählung in Thüringen," *Zeitschrift für die gesamte Neurologie und Psychiatrie*, Vol. 133 (1931), 352-390; "Psychiatrische Bestandesaufnahme im Gebiete eines medizinisch-anthropologischen Zensus in der Nähe von Rosenheim,"

Zeitschrift für die gesamte Neurologie und Psychiatrie, Vol. 160 (1938), 189-201.

30. Erik Strömgren, "Beitraege Zur Psychiatrischen Erblehre," *Acta Psychiatrica et Neurologica, Supplementum 19*, (Copenhagen: Ejnar Munksgaard, 1938), 259.

31. We were greatly aided in our use of the Baltimore data by Drs. Paul Lemkau and Chrisopher Tietze. Their findings were published with Marcia Cooper's in "Mental Hygiene Problems in an Urban District," *Mental Hygiene*, Vol. 25 (1941), 624-646; Vol. 26 (1942), 100-119.

32. William F. Roth, Jr. and Frank H. Luton, "The Mental Health Problem in Tennessee," *The American Journal of Psychiatry*, Vol. 99, No. 5 (March, 1943), 662-675.

33. Torsten Sjögren, "Genetic-Statistical and Psychiatric Investigations of a West-Swedish Population," *Acta Psychiatrica et Neurologica, Supplementum 52* (Copenhagen: Ejnar Munksgaard, 1948). Dr. Sjögren also furnished additional data by correspondence. He has made a similar study of a second Swedish island; the results of this investigation will be published in the near future.

34. J. A. Böök's findings are being published under the title, "A Genetic and Neuro-Psychiatric Investigation of a North-Swedish Population," *Acta Genetica et Statistica Medica*, Vol. 4, No. 1 (1953-54). Dr. Böök graciously furnished the information used in this study from a preliminary report of his findings.

35. Johan Bremer, "A Social Psychiatric Investigation of a Small Community in Northern Norway," *Acta Psychiatrica et Neurologica, Supplementum 62* (1951), 1-166.

36. Tsung-yi Lin, "A Study of the Incidence of Mental Disorder in Chinese and Other Cultures," *Psychiatry*, Vol. 16, No. 4, pp. 313-336.

37. Paul Lemkau, Christopher Tietze, and Marcia Cooper, "A Survey of Statistical Studies on the Prevalence and Incidence of Mental Disorder in Sample Populations," *Public Health Reports*, Vol. 58, No. 53 (December 31, 1943), 18.

38. Biometrics Branch, National Institute of Mental Health, "Patients in Mental Institutions 1948," *U. S. Public Health Service Publication 89* (Washington, D.C.: U.S. Government Printing Office, 1951), 9.

39. According to a personal communication from Dr. Kurt H. Fremming.

40. Descriptions in English of the Abridged Method of Weinberg and its modifications can be found in Franz J. Kallmann, *The Genetics of Schizophrenia* (New York: J. J. Augustin, 1938), pp. 99-142; also Torsten Sjögren, *op. cit.*, pp. 53-56.

41. The Milbank Memorial Fund, *An Epidemiology of Mental Disorder* (New York, 1950), p. 41.

42. Örnulv Ödegaard, "Emigration and Insanity," *Acta Psychiatrica et Neurologica, Supplementum 4*, (Copenhagen: Levin & Munksgaard, 1932), pp. 51-52.

43. United Nations Demographic Yearbook, 1952, Table 17.

44. Roth and Luton, *op. cit.*, p. 669.

45. Sjögren, *op. cit.*, pp. 19-20.

46. Benjamin Malzberg, *Social and Biological Aspects of Mental Disease* (Utica, N. Y.; New York State Hospital Press, 1940), p. 11.

47. James L. Halliday, *Psychosocial Medicine* (New York: W. W. Norton & Co., 1948), p. 66.

48. Goldhamer and Marshall, *op. cit.*, p. 120.

49. Ödegaard, *op. cit.*, p. 206.

50. Faris and Dunham, *op. cit.*, pp. 163-169.

51. August B. Hollingshead and Frederick C. Redlich, "Social Stratification and Schizophrenia," *American Sociological Review*. Vol. 19, No. 3 (1954), 302-306.

52. Albert Deutsch, "Recent Trends in Mental Hospital Care," *Social Work in the Current Scene, 1950*. Selected Papers, National Conference of Social Work (New York: Columbia University Press, 1950), p. 147.

53. Kurt H. Fremming, *The Expectation of Mental Infirmity in a Sample of the Danish Population*, p. 28.

54. Christopher Tietze, Paul Lemkau, and Marcia Cooper, "Schizophrenic, Manic-Depressive Psychosis and Social-Economic Status," *The American Journal of Sociology*, Vol. 47, No. 2 (September, 1941), 167-175.

55. Frieda Fromm-Reichmann, "Intensive Psychotherapy of Manic-Depressives," *Confinia Neurologica*, Vol. 9 (1949), 159.

56. J. C. Carothers, *The African Mind in Health and Disease* (Geneva: World Health Organization, 1953), pp. 142-148.

57. Federal Security Agency, Public Health Service, National Institute of Mental Health, *Patients in Mental Institutions, 1949* (Washington, D.C.: U.S. Government Printing Office, 1952) Table 8, p. 39; Table 9, p. 43.

58. Faris and Dunham, *op. cit.*, p. 172. Also David J. Merrill, "Inheritance of Manic-Depressive Psychoses," *A.M.A. Archives of Neurology*, Vol. 66, (September, 1951) 272-279.

59. Kallman, *The Genetics of Schizophrenia*, p. 291.

60. Tietze, Lemkau, and Cooper, *op. cit.*, p. 168.

61. Goldhamer and Marshall, *op. cit.*, Part I.

62. Bremer, *op. cit.*, Chap. X.

63. Horatio M. Pollock, "Statistical Review of Mental Disorders in Later Life," *Mental Disorders in Later Life*, ed. Oscar J. Kaplan (Palo Alto: Stanford University Press, 1945), p. 7.

64. James C. Coleman, *Abnormal Psychology and Modern Life* (Chicago: Scott, Foresman & Co., 1950), p. 279.

65. *Ibid.*, p. 294. This recovery ratio is also closer to that reported by Lundquist for *depressed* manic-depressives (79.6 per cent) as opposed to *manic* cases (92.2 per cent). See Gunnar Lundquist "Prognosis and Course in Manic-Depressive Psychosis," *Acta Psychiatrica et Neurologica*, *Supplementum 35*, (Copenhagen: Ejnar Munksgaard, 1945).

66. Lloyd H. Ziegler and Philip H. Heersema, "A Follow-Up Study of One Hundred and Eleven Non-Hospitalized Depressed Patients after Fourteen Years," *American Journal of Psychiatry*, Vol. 99 (May, 1943), 813-817.

67. Thomas A. C. Rennie, with the help of J. B. Fowler, "Prognosis in Manic-Depressive Psychoses," *American Journal of Psychiatry*, Vol. 98 (May, 1942), 801-814.

68. Otto Fenichel, *The Psychoanalytic Theory of Neurosis* (New York: W. W. Norton & Co., 1945), p. 415.

69. *Mental Disorders, Diagnostic and Statistical Manual* (Washington, D. C.: American Psychiatric Association Mental Hospital Service, 1952), p. 26.

70. Mimeographed release of the Federal Security Agency, u.d.

71. Federal Security Agency, Public Health Service, *Patients in Mental Institutions 1948*, and the same report for 1949 (Washington, D.C.: U.S. Government Printing Office), Public Health Service Publication No. 89, Table 8, p. 38; and No. 233, 1952, Table 8, p. 39.

72. Bremer, *op. cit.*, pp. 50-51.

73. Tsung-Yi-Lin, *op. cit.*, pp. 333-334.

74. Roth and Luton, *op. cit.*, p. 671; Lemkau, Tietze, and Cooper, "Mental Hygiene Problems in an Urban District, Fourth Paper," *Mental Hygiene*, Vol. 27, No. 2 (April, 1943), 279-295.

75. Russell Fraser, *The Incidence of Neurosis among Factory Workers* (London: H.M.S.O., 1947), pp. 5-6.

76. Jacob Schwartz and Elvin V. Semrad, "Psychosomatic Disorders in Psychoses," *Psychosomatic Medicine*, Vol. 13 (1951), 314-321.

77. Andreas Erenpreiss, *Ein Sendbrief*, Anno 1652. Printed in German for the Hutterite Brethren in Scottsdale, Pa., 1920; mimeographed in English, trans. by John P. Liebe (Poplar Point, Manitoba: Poplar Point Hutterite Community, n.d.) 64-65.

78. A. R. Mangus, *Mental Health of Rural Children in Ohio* (Wooster: Ohio Agricultural Experiment Station, Research Bulletin 682, March, 1949). He defines adjustment in terms of test scores of children on a battery of paper-pencil objective tests.

79. W. W. Ludeman and J. R. McAnelly, "Intelligence of Colony People," *Journal of Educational Policy*, Vol. 21, No. 7 (October, 1930), 612-615.

80. John Dollard and Neal E. Miller, *Personality and Psychotherapy* (New York: McGraw-Hill, 1950).

81. *Diagnostic and Statistical Manual, op. cit.*, p. 34.

82. Weinberg, *op. cit.*, p. 260.

83. Clark, "The Hutterian Communities," *op. cit.*, p. 483.

84. Deets, *op. cit.*, p. 2.

85. Fremming, *op. cit.*, p. 36.

86. Vol. 23, No. 1 (1952), 11.

87. Alfred C. Kinsey, W. S. Pomeroy, and C. E. Martin, *Sexual Behavior in the Human Male* (Philadelphia: W. B. Saunders & Co., 1948): Alfred C. Kinsey, W. S. Pomeroy, C. E. Martin and P. H. Gebhard, *Sexual Behavior in the Human Female* (Philadelphia: W. B. Saunders & Co., 1953).

88. Albert Einstein and Sigmund Freud, *Why War?* (League of Nations, International Institute of Intellectual Co-operation, 1933), p. 47.

89. Bert Kaplan and Thomas F. A. Plaut, "Hutterite Culture and Mental Health," (Unpublished ms., Department of Social Relations, Harvard University, February 1953), p. 47.

90. Merton, *op. cit.*

91. Louis J. Karnosh, with the collaboration of Edward M. Zucker, *A Handbook of Psychiatry* (St. Louis: C. V. Mosby Co., 1945), p. 197.

92. Theodore H. Ingalls, "Mongolism," *Scientific American*, Vol. 186, No. 2 (February, 1952), 60-66.

93. A. F. Tredgold, *Mental Deficiency* (8th ed.; Baltimore: Williams & Wilkins Co., 1953), pp. 11-19.

94. Johan A. Böök, *A Genetic and Neuropsychiatric Investigation of a North-Swedish Population, Acta Genetica et Statistica Medica*, Vol. 14, No. 4 (Basle: 1953), 347.

95. Tredgold, *op. cit.*, p. 16.

96. Herbert Yahraes, *Epilepsy—The Ghost Is Out of the Closet* (New York: Public Affairs Committee, Inc., Pamphlet No. 98, 1944), p. 4.

97. Jerry C. Price, Kate Levine Kogan, and Lois R. Tompkins, "The Prevalence and Incidence of Extramural Epilepsy," *Epilepsy*, ed. by Paul H. Hoch and Robert P. Knight (New York: Grune & Stratton, 1947), p. 49.

98. Benjamin Malzberg, "The Incidence and Prevalence of Intramural Epilepsy," *ibid.*, pp. 42-47.

99. Earl Lemon Koos, *Families in Trouble* (Morningside Heights, New York: King's Crown Press, 1946). Lee R. Steiner, *Where Do People Take Their Troubles?* (Boston: Houghton Mifflin, 1945).

100. Zieglschmid, *Das Klein Geschichtsbuch der Hutterischen Brüder*, pp. 110, 388, 423; Horsch, *op. cit.*, pp. 37-38.

101. August B. Hollingshead and Frederick C. Redlich, "Social Stratification and Psychiatric Disorders," *American Sociological Review*, Vol. 18, No. 2 (April, 1953), 163.

102. Erenpreiss, *op. cit.*, pp. 62-63.

103. Dollard and Miller, *op. cit.*, pp. 445-459.

104. Clarence Oberndorf, *1949 Yearbook of Psychoanalysis* (New York: International Universities Press), p. 11; Lillian Blumberg, "Does Psychoanalysis Cure?" *Commentary*, Vol. 10 (1950), 486. Some studies of this question are now in process or were completed recently: E. L. Kelly and D. W. Fiske, *The Prediction of Performance in Clinical Psychology* (Ann Arbor: University of Michigan Press, 1951); Robert R. Holt and Lester Luborsky, "Research in the Selection of Psychiatrists: A Second Interim Report," *Bulletin of the Menninger Clinic*, Vol. 16, No. 4 (July, 1952), 125; Edwin Powers and Helen Witmer, *An Experiment in the Prevention of Delinquency* (New York: Columbia University Press, 1951); J. McVicker Hunt, Margaret Blenkner, and Leonard S. Kogan, *Testing Results in Social Casework* (New York: F.S.S.A., 1950); Leonard S. Kogan, J. McVicker Hunt, and Phyllis F. Bartelme, *A Follow-Up Study of the Results of Social Casework* (New York: F.S.S.A., 1953); Carl Rogers and Rosalind F. Dymond, eds., *Psychotherapy and Personality Change*, (Chicago: University of Chicago Press, 1954); Morris B. Perloff, "An Analysis of Therapeutic Relationships in a Group Therapy Setting" (Unpublished Ph.D. dissertation, Western Reserve University, June, 1953).

105. Robert R. Sears, "Survey of Objective Studies of Psychoanalytic Concepts," *Social Science Research Council Bulletin 51* (1943), pp. 1-156; H. Warren Dunham, "Social Psychiatry," *American Sociological Review*, Vol. 13, No. 5 (April, 1948), 183-197.

106. Bertha M. Shambaugh, *The Community of True Inspiration* (Iowa City: Iowa State Historical Society, 1908); also by the same author, "Amana in Transition," *Palimpsest*, Vol. 17, No. 5 (May, 1936), 149-184.

107. George Orwell, *1984* (New York: Harcourt Brace, 1949): Aldous L. Huxley, *Brave New World* (New York: Harper & Bros., 1950).

REFERENCES [253]

108. Sigmund Freud, *Moses and Monotheism* (New York: Alfred A. Knopf, 1939), p. 193.

109. Margaret Mead, "Some Relationships Between Social Anthropology and Psychiatry," *Dynamic Psyciatry*, ed. Franz Alexander and Helen Ross (Chicago: University of Chicago Press, 1952), pp. 401-448.

110. Deutsch, *op. cit.*, p. 158.

111. Horatio M. Pollock, *Family Care of Mental Patients* (Utica: New York State Hospital Press, 1936).

112. J. Mayone Stycos, "Family Care—Neglected Area of Research," *Psychiatry*, Vol. 14, No. 3 (August, 1951), 301-306.

113. Joseph W. Eaton and Robert J. Weil, "Psychotherapeutic Principles in Social Research—an Interdisciplinary Study of the Hutterites," *Psychiatry*, Vol. 14, No. 4 (November, 1951); Joseph W. Eaton, "Social Processes of Professional Teamwork," *American Sociological Review*, Vol. 16, No. 5 (October, 1951).

114. Abram Kardiner and Lionel Ovesey, *The Mark of Oppression* (New York: W. W. Norton & Co., 1951).

115. W. I. Thomas and Florian Znaniecki, *The Polish Peasant in Europe and America* (New York: Alfred A. Knopf, 1927).

116. Joseph W. Eaton, "The Assessment of Mental Health," *American Journal of Psychiatry*, Vol. 108, No. 2 (August, 1951), 81-90.

117. Salmon Ganzfried, *Code of Jewish Law (Kitzur Schulchan-Aruch)*, trans. from Hebrew by Hyman E. Goldin (New York: Star Hebrew Book Co., 1928).

118. See Georges Gurvitch, *Sociology of Law* (New York: Philosophical Library, 1942), pp. 106-122, for a detailed treatment of Durkheim's contributions to the sociology of law.

119. Horsch, *op. cit.*, pp. 75-78.

120. *Ibid.*, p. 107.

121. Zieglschmid, *op. cit.*, pp. 422-435.

122. "An Act Respecting Lands in the Province Held as Communal Property," Revised in 1947, Chapter 16, Assented to March 31, 1947, Government of Alberta. See also: Joseph W. Eaton, "Canada's Scapegoats," *The Nation*, Vol. 169, No. 11 (1949), 253-254.

123. Bill B., The Senate of Canada, *An Act to Incorporate the Hutterian Church*, passed by the Senate, February 14, 1951, 5 pp. See also: *Constitution of Hutterian Brethren Church and Rules as to Community Property* (Winnipeg: published by E. A. Fletcher, Barrister-Solicitor, n.d.), 14 pp.

124. E. V. Stonequist, *The Marginal Man* (New York: Charles Scribner's Sons, 1937).

125. Kurt Lewin, "Psycho-Sociological Problems of a Minority Group," *Resolving Social Conflicts* (New York: Harper & Bros., 1948), pp. 145-158.

126. A study in process at Yale University under the joint direction of Drs. A. B. Hollingshead and F. E. Redlich. It is sponsored by the National Institute of Mental Health.

127. Ernest Jones, "The Concept of a Normal Mind," *International Journal of Psychoanalysis*. Vol. 23 (1942), 1-8.

128. A. B. Hollingshead and F. C. Redlich, eds., *Proceedings of the Conference on Community Structure and Psychiatric Disorders* (held

under the auspices of the Milbank Memorial Fund, June 11-12, 1952),
mimeographed report, 1953.

129. Coleman, *op. cit.*, p. 657.

130. Prepared by the Committee on Nomenclature and Statistics of
the American Psychiatric Association, *op. cit.*, p. 130.

131. Joseph W. Eaton, *Exploring Tomorrow's Agriculture* (New York:
Harper & Bros., 1943) pp. 218-230.

132. *Patients in Mental Institutions, 1948,* Table 8, p. 38.

133. Estimated incidence of functional cases seen by general practitioners and in general clinics made by Rowntree, Mittelmann, Rymer,
Heldt, Ebaugh, Smith, and Hightower, in *Statistics Pertinent to Psychiatry
in the United States* (Group for the Advancement of Psychiatry, Report
No. 7, March, 1949), 2.

134. Sjögren, *op. cit.*

135. *Ibid.*

136. Kallmann, *op. cit.*

137. *Collaborative Research in Psychopathology* (Topeka: The Committee on Psychopathology of the Group for the Advancement of Psychiatry, Report No. 25, January, 1954).

BOOKS PUBLISHED BY

The Free Press